THE CHARLTON
STANDARD CATALOGUE OF

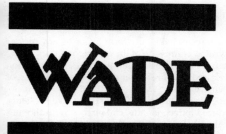

Volume Three: Tableware
Second Edition

By
Pat Murray

Publisher
W. K. Cross

The Charlton Press

TORONTO, ONTARIO ◆ BIRMINGHAM, MICHIGAN

Canadian Cataloguing in Publication Data
Murray, Pat
    The Charlton standard catalogue of Wade

2nd ed.
Previously published under title: Pre-war and more Wades.
Includes index.
v.1. General Issues - v.2. Decorative ware - v.3. Tableware.
ISBN 0-88968-183- X (v.3)

1. George Wade and Son—Catalogs.
2. Figurines —England — Catalogs.
3. Miniature pottery—England—Catalogs.
I. Title. II. Title: Pre-war and more Wades.

NK8473.5.W33M8   738.8'2   C95-932732-0

**Printed in Canada
in the Province of Ontario**

EDITORIAL

Editor	Nicola Leedham
Assistant Editor	Jean Dale

ACKNOWLEDGEMENTS

The Charlton Press wishes to thank those who have assisted with the second edition of the *Charlton Standard Catalogue of Wade: Volume Three, Tableware.*

Special Thanks

The publisher and author would like to thank the staff and retired staff of the George Wade & Son Ltd. and Wade Heath Ltd. potteries (now Wade Ceramics Limited) and the Wade (Ireland) Ltd. Pottery (Now Seagoe Ceramics Ltd.) Cynthia Risby and Jenny Wright of the Wade Shop, for sending me copies of sales leaflet's and original prices and for answering my many questions; J.A. Stringer of Seagoe Ceramics Ltd., for Irish Wade Advertising leaflets.

I would like to dedicate this book to my husband, Gordon.

Contributors to the Second Edition

Many thanks to **Peter and Lesley Chisholm**, Perthshire, Scotland; **Marion and Gareth Hunt**, Aberdeenshire, Scotland; and **Pam and Brian Powell**, Aberdeenshire, Scotland for their hospitality during our stay with each of them and for allowing us to photograph their collections.

Averill Abbott, U.S.A.; **Terry Austin**, U.K.; **Barrie Reference Library**, Ontario, Canada; **The British Newspaper Library**, London, England; **Camtrak**, U.K.; **A. Clark**, U.K.; **Elizabeth and John Clarke**, U.K.; **Ellen Clayton**, Canada; **Francis Davis**, Canada; **Betty and Alex Dyce**, Canada; **Janet and Mike Evans**, Yesterdays, U.K.; **Tom Fish**, U.S.A.; **Peggy Fyffe**, U.S.A.; **Betty and Dennis Hannigan**, U.S.A.; **Freda Harker**, U.S.A.; **Charlie Harlan**, U.S.A.; **Camille Huggins**, U.S.A.; **Annie Jamieson**, U.S.A.; **Peg and Roger Johnson**, U.S.A.; **Mark Justice**, U.S.A.; **Delores Kennet**, U.S.A.; **Esther Kramer**, U.S.A.; **Larry Larson**, U.S.A.; **Dave Lee**, U.K.; **Jane Lister**, U.K.; **Joanne and Don Mandryk**, Canada; **Pam and John Marshall**, U.S.A.; **Michael A. Matthew**, U.S.A.; **Shannon McLandish**, U.S.A.; **Metro Toronto Reference Library**, Ontario, Canada; **Mark Oliver**, Phillips Auctioneers and Valuers, U.K.; **June Rance**, U.K.; **Janet Robinson**, New Zealand; **John Royal**, U.S.A.; **Gary Scott**, U.S.A.; **Mary Ann and Robert Sloan**, U.S.A.; **Stroud Public Library**, Ontario, Canada; **Kim and Derek Watson,** U.K.; **Carol and John Woolner**, Canada; **Jo Ann Yadro**, U.S.A; **Mary and Steve Yager**, U.S.A.; **I. and R. Yallop**.

And my thanks to all the Wade Collectors who have helped with information and photographs for this book and preferred not to have their names mentioned.

A SPECIAL NOTE TO COLLECTORS

We welcome and appreciate any comments or suggestions in regard to the *Charlton Standard Catalogue of Wade Tableware*. If you would like to participate in pricing, please contact Jean Dale at the Charlton Press. To provide new information or corrections, please write to Pat Murray, Box 746, RR #2, Stroud, Ontario L0L 2M0, Canada.

The Charlton Press

Editorial Office
2040 Yonge Street, Suite 208
Toronto, Ontario, M4S 1Z9
Tel: (800) 442-6042 Fax: (800) 442-1542
Tel: (416) 488-1418 Fax: (416) 488-4656
www.charltonpress.com e-mail: chpress@charltonpress.com

FORWARD

For this Wade Collectors book I have listed all the early domestic products of the John Wade (later to become) the Wadeheath "Royal Victoria Pottery", the George Wade Pottery and Wade Ireland Pottery. Although mainly domestic type pottery, it is collectable in its own right due to the attractive colours and novelty designs and shapes used. These domestic pieces are collected by adults rather than children but a lot of young Wade collectors have parts of or a complete set of children's Disney tea sets and other cartoon character tea sets in their collections.

HOW TO USE THIS CATALOGUE

THE PURPOSE

This publication has been designed to serve two specific purposes. Its first purpose is to furnish the collector with accurate and detailed listings that provide the essential information needed to build a rewarding collection. Its second function is to provide collectors and dealers with current market prices for the complete line of Wade tablewares.

STYLES AND VERSIONS

STYLES: A change in style occurs when a major element of the design is altered or modified as a result of a deliberate mould change. An example of this is Orb Style One and Orb Style Two.

VERSIONS: Versions are modifications in a minor style element of the piece, such as the different handles on Orb jugs and teapots.

VARIATIONS: A variation indicates a change in the colour or pattern in the design; for example, the variations in the Gingham design.

THE LISTINGS

A Word On Pricing

The purpose of this catalogue is to give readers the most accurate, up-to-date retail prices for Wade tablewares in the markets of the United States, Canada and the United Kingdom. However, one must remember that these prices are indications only and that the actual selling price may be higher or lower by the time the final transaction agreement is reached.

To accomplish this The Charlton Press continues to access an international pricing panel of Wade experts who submit prices based on both dealer and collector retail price activity, as well as current auction results in U.S., Canadian, and U.K. markets. These market figures are carefully averaged to reflect accurate valuations for the Wade items listed herein in each of these three markets.

Please be aware that prices given in a particular currency are for models in that country only. The prices published herein have not been calculated using exchange rates—they have been determined solely by the supply and demand within the country in question.

A necessary word of caution. No pricing catalogue can be, or should be, a fixed price list. This catalogue should be considered as a guide only, one that shows the most current retail prices based on market demand within a particular region.

A Word on Condition

The prices published herein are for items in mint condition. Collectors are cautioned that a repaired or restored piece may be worth as little as 50 percent of the value of the same piece in mint condition. Those collectors interested strictly in investment potential must avoid damaged items.

All relevant information must be known about an item in order to make a proper valuation. When comparing auction prices to catalogue prices, collectors and dealers should remember two important points. First, to compare "apples and apples," be sure that auction prices include a buyer's premium, if one is due. Prices realized for models in auction catalogues may not include this additional cost. Secondly, if an item is restored or repaired, it may not be noted in the listing, and as a result, the price will not be reflective of that same piece in mint condition.

Technical Information

On the pages that follow Wade models are listed, illustrated, described and priced. The items are categorized by type, i.e. Tea Sets, Coffee Sets, Bowls, Plates, Children's Tea Sets etc., then arranged alphabetically by shape name (if known). Within each shape, the items are further broken down by design name.

The measurements of the models are given in millimetres. Most items are measured according to their **height**. For relatively flat objects—bowls, dishes and plates—the measurement listed is the **diameter** of a round item.

Although the publisher has made every attempt to obtain and photograph all models listed, several pieces, naturally, have not come into the publisher's possession.

CONTENTS

INTRODUCTION

The Wade Heath Royal Victoria Pottery (formerly Wade and Co.) was originally founded by a furniture maker, John Wade who had followed his father (also named John) into the furniture trade. In the mid-1800s however, the younger John Wade began to see that there was more profit to be made in pottery production, an already well-established art in the Staffordshire towns where the essential ingredients of clay and felspar were found in the soil of the surrounding countryside. Thus, John Wade turned his interest and his talent to this trade.

In 1867 John joined in partnership with James and Henry Colclough and they began trading under the names of "Wade and Colclough." Later the name was changed to "John Wade & Co." The pottery was known as the "Toy Works." John's nephew William Wade also worked for Wade & Colclough and John, who had no children of his own, took William under his wing and taught him the pottery business. Their main production at that time was Teapots and their accompaniments — teapot stands, sugar bowls and water and milk jugs, etc. As these early items were intended for domestic use they were produced in a dark heavy earthenware china rather than the whiter and lighter porcelain the English Wade Potteries are now famous for.

It was some twenty years later, in 1887, that John Wade broke with the Colcloughs and left to form his own pottery, with his nephew William and William's brother, Albert J Wade. The pottery was renamed "Wade & Co." and used the trademarks of an impressed "WADES" and also an ink stamped "W and Co B." The "B" stood for Burslem and it was added to distinguish the W & Co. mark from another pottery, "Whittaker & Co" of Hanley, Staffordshire, which used the same "W & Co" trademark.

John and his nephews expanded their "Toy Works" pottery and purchased the "High Street Works" pottery which was situated next door to the "Toy Works." In 1888, William and Albert formed "J & W. Wade & Co" which specialised in the manufacture of tiles for fireplace surrounds, floors and walls. In 1891 the "J & W Wade & Co" pottery was christened the "Flaxman Tile Works."

William Wade retired from the pottery business and in 1913 went to live in California where he died in a freak car accident when returning from the funeral of A.J. Wades brother-in-law Francis Stoker in 1914. Francis, with William Wade's help and advice, had intended to start a pottery in Los Angeles, California.

In 1927 Albert J. Wade, who had, on the death of his uncle John and his brother William, inherited the "Wade & Co" and the "Flaxman Tile Work" potteries, formed a new company with a friend George Heath and changed the name of "Wade & Co" to "Wade Heath & Co." The main items produced by this partnership were domestic and decorative products.

The "Flaxman Tile Works," which was still owned and operated by Albert J. Wade, carried on its business of producing tiles and fireplace surrounds until, with the ever growing popularity of gas fires in Britain, ceramic fireplace surrounds and tiles were no longer a viable product and the "Flaxman Tile works" finally ceased trading in 1970.

In 1933 Albert Wade died, and his nephew George Albert Wade, later to become Sir George Wade and founder of the "George Wade & Son" Pottery now famous for its "Whimsies," became Chairman of the "A.J. Wade Ltd. Flaxman Tile Works" and "Wade Heath & Co Ltd." with George Heath as managing director.

In 1938 the "Wade Heath & Co Ltd." pottery was moved to a new location at the "Royal Victoria Pottery" in Westport Road, Burslem. With the death of Sir George Wade at the age of 94 in 1986, and the early death of his son George Anthony Wade from leukaemia a year later in 1987, the Wade Potteries were taken over by "Beauford Engineering PLC." The Wade Potteries were renamed "Wade Ceramics Ltd." The former "Wade Heath/Royal Victoria Pottery" is still in production today under it's new name of "Wade Ceramics."

1947 saw the acquisition of a Pottery in Northern Ireland, which in 1950 was named "Wade (Ulster) Ltd." The pottery concentrated on the production of industrial wares such as electrical insulators for telephone poles.

In 1953, "Wade (Ulster) Ltd." was asked to fill an order for "Coronation Tankards" which the "Wade Heath" and "George Wade" potteries could not fill due to Government restrictions. With the success of their tankards with their distinctive "Irish" glaze, the Ulster pottery branched out into new fields of Giftware and Domestic Tableware production.

In 1966 the Pottery was renamed "Wade Ireland Ltd." and continued giftware production until 1986, when they reverted back to Industrial Wares and Tableware production.

"Wade Ireland" was taken over by "Beauford Engineering PLC" upon the death of George Anthony Wade and was renamed "Seagoe Ceramics" in 1990. Seagoe continued to manufacture domestic tablewares until 1992 when its production reverted back to industrial ceramics.

BACKSTAMPS

THE WADE POTTERIES, c.1887-1996

1. **WITHOUT WADE NAME**

A. **EMBOSSED**
a) "Made in England"

B. **IMPRESSED**
a) "Made in England" (c.1930), with or without registration mark

C. **INK STAMPS**
Black:
a) "England" (c.1938)
b) "Made In England" (c.1938-c.1942)
c) "Made in England" with letter A, B or J added (c.1939-1945)

2. "WADES"

A. **EMBOSSED**
a) Registered "Diamond" (c.1867-1887)

B. **IMPRESSED**
a) "Wades" (c.1887-1890)

C. **INK STAMPS**
Black:
a) "W & Co B" with or without design name (c.1887-1900)

b) "Wades England" (c.1900-1927)
Orange:
a) "Wades England" with lion (c.1927-1933)

b) "Wades Orcadia Ware" with lion (c.1933)

3. "WADEHEATH" (one word)

A. **INK STAMPS**
Black:
a) "Flaxman Ware Hand Made Pottery by Wadeheath England" (c.1935-1937) with or without design name

b) "Wadeheath by permission Walt Disney England" (c.1935-1940)
c) "Wadeheath England" with letter A, B or J added (c.1939-1945)
d) "Wadeheath England" with lion (c.1934-1937)

e) "Wadeheath Orcadia Ware British Made" (c.1934-1935)

f) "Wadeheath Ware by permission Walt Disney Mickey Mouse Ltd. Made in England" (c.1935)
g) "Wadeheath Ware England" (c.1934-1937)

h) "Wadeheath Ware made in England manufactured by permission Walt Disney Mickey Mouse LTD" (c.1935)

Orange:
a) "Wadeheath England" with lion (c.1933-1934)
b) "Wadeheath Orcadia Ware" (c.1933-1934)

4. "WADE HEATH" (two words)

A. INK STAMPS

Black:
a) "England" (c.1937-1940)
b) "Flaxman Wade Heath England" (c.1937-1939) with or without design name added

c) "Wade Heath England" (rounded W 1937-1940)

d) "Wade Heath England" (rounded W) with letter A, B or J added (c.1939-1945)
e) "Wade Heath England" (straight W c.1945)
f) "Wade Heath England J" (straight W c.1942-c.1945)

Green:
a) "Wade Heath England" (rounded W 1937-1940)
b) "Wade Heath England" (rounded W) with letter A, B or J added (c.1939-1945)
c) "Wade Heath England" (straight W c.1945)
d) "Wade Heath England J" (straight W c.1942-c.1945)

5. "WADE"

A. INK STAMPS

Black:
a) Circular "Royal Victoria Pottery Wade England" (c.1952-c.1965)

b) "Wade Bramble England" (c.1950-1953)

c) "Wade England Flaxman" (c.1945-c.1948)
d) "Wade England" (crossed W c.1948-1953)

Green:
a) "Wade England" (crossed W c.1948-1953) (with or without design name)

b) "Wade England" with letter A, B or J added (crossed W c.1942-c.1945)

B. TRANSFER PRINTED

Black:
a) "Wade" between two lines (with or without design name)
b) "Wade" (c.1990-1993) (with or without design/designer name)
c) "Wade England" (with or without design/designer name)

d) "Wade Staffordshire England" (c.1982-1986) (with or without design name)
e) "Genuine Wade Porcelain" (c.1982)
f) "Wade Potteries PLC" (c.1989) (with or without design name)
g) "Designed Exclusively for Boots by Wade Ceramics" (c.1990-1991) (with or without design/designer name)
h) "Wade England" with two lines (c.1990-present) (with or without design name)
i) "Wade made in England" (1991) (with or without design name)

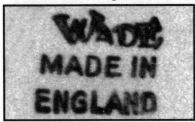

Gold:
a) Circular "Royal Victoria Pottery Wade England" (c.1960-1970)

b) Semi circular "Wade made in England Hand Painted" (c.1953-c.1962) (with or without design name)

c) "Wade made in England Hand Painted" (c.1955-c.1962) (with or without design name)

Green:
a) "Wade England" (c.1961)

Red:
a) Wade England" (c.1953 - c.1962)
b) Semi Circular "Royal Victoria Pottery Staffordshire Wade England" (c.1980-c.1988)

Silver:
a) Semi circular "Wade made in England Hand Painted" (c.1953)

WADE IRELAND, c.1952-1991

A. EMBOSSED

a) "Irish Porcelain (curved over shamrock) Made in Ireland by Wade Co. Armagh" in straight lines (c.1952-c.1989)
b) "Made in Ireland Porcelain - Wade - eire tire a dheanta" (c.1971-c.1989) (no "Irish")
c) "Made in Ireland by Wade" in straight line (c.1970)
d) "Wade Porcelain Made In Ireland" (c.1970)

e) "Irish Porcelain (curved over large shamrock and crown)
f) Wade Ireland" in straight line (c.1975-1987)

Circular:
a) "Celtic Porcelain by Wade Ireland" in Irish Knot wreath (c.1965)
b) "Irish Porcelain (centre shamrock) made in Ireland" (with potters initial included) (c.1952-c.1989)

c) "Irish Porcelain (curved over shamrock) Wade Ireland" in straight line (c.1975-1987)
d) "Irish Porcelain Wade Made in Ireland" with shamrock and crown in the centre (c.1982-c.1986)
f) "Made in Ireland Irish Porcelain (central small shamrock and crown) Wade eire tira dheanta" (c.1971-1976)

Curved:
a) "Irish Porcelain" over straight "Made in Ireland" (c.1975-1987)

Oval:
a) "Shamrock Pottery Made in Ireland" (c.1956-1989)

b) "Irish Porcelain (over a small Shamrock) Made in Ireland" in Irish Knot wreath (with or without designers name added under the wreath) (c.1962)

B. IMPRESSED

a) Hand written "(number of ounces) W.G. White London" with impressed "Wade Porcelain Co. Armagh" (on Caviar Pots)
b) "Irish Porcelain (curved over large shamrock) Made in Ireland" in straight line (c.1955-c.1979)
c) "Irish Porcelain (slanted over shamrock) Wade Co Armagh" in straight line (c.1955)
d) "Irish Porcelain (curved over shamrock) Made in Ireland" (with potters initial included) (c.1952-c.1989)

e) "Irish Porcelain (curved over large shamrock and crown) Wade Ireland" in straight line (c.1982-1987)
f) "Irish Porcelain (curved over shamrock with or without potters initial in shamrock) Made in England" (c.1980-c.1989)
g) "Made in Ireland by Wade"

Circular:
a) "Irish Porcelain (curved over shamrock) Made in Ireland by Wade Co. Armagh" in straight lines (c.1950-c.1989)

b) "Irish Porcelain (shamrock in centre) made in Ireland" (potters initial included) (c.1955-1969)

C.   INK STAMPS

Black:
a) "Irish Porcelain (centre Shamrock) Made in Ireland" (c.1960-c.1989)

Green:
a) Circular "Seagoe Ceramics Wade 91 Ireland" (1991)

D.   TRANSFER PRINTED

Black:
a) "Irish Porcelain (slanted over shamrock) Wade Co Armagh" in straight line (c.1955)
b) "Irish Porcelain (curved over shamrock) Wade County Armagh" in straight line (c.1960-c.1989)
c) "Wade Ireland" (c.1970)
d) "Irish Porcelain (centre shamrock and crown) Wade Made in Ireland" (c1985-1990)
e) "Irish Porcelain (centre shamrock and crown) Wade Ireland" (c1985-1990)

Black Circular:
a) "Celtic Porcelain made in Ireland by Wade Co. Armagh" (1965)
b) "Made in Ireland Porcelain Wade eire tir A dheanta" (c.1978-c.1982)

Blue:
a) Semi circular "Made In Ireland Wade Classic Linen eire tir A dheanta"

Green Circular:
a) "Made in Ireland Porcelain Wade eire tir A dheanta" (1983-1986)

Green Oval:
a) "Shamrock Pottery made in Ireland" (c.1956-1961)

TABLEWARE SETS
1927-1998

SHAPE NAME INDEX

ALBERT SHAPE, 1984-1995

These round, straight- sided teapots have a large round finial on the lid, which sits inside the rim. The rounded handle has a thumb rest. The first Albert shaped teapot was produced for Boots the Chemist in 1984 with a poppy flower design. There are two versions of Albert mugs. The first version is larger and has a more compact handle.

BON APPETITE DESIGN, 1989

This set was produced for British Home Stores, a chain of British department stores.

Backstamp: Printed "BhS Bon Appetit Tableware made in Britain"

No.	Description	Colourways	Size	U.S. $	Can. $	U.K. £
1	Cream jug	White; multi-coloured print	95	12.00	15.00	8.00
2	Sugar bowl		65	12.00	15.00	8.00
3	Teapot, 6-cup		165	40.00	50.00	25.00
4	Utensil jar		156	12.00	15.00	8.00

CAT BURGLAR DESIGN, 1989

This design, with a masked cat sitting in an armchair eating cake, was produced for Boots the Chemist in 1989.

Photograph of design
not available
at press time

Backstamp: Printed "Wade" with two lines

No.	Description	Colourways	Size	U.S. $	Can. $	U.K. £
1	Biscuit barrel, small	White; masked ginger cat; black/white striped jersey; pink armchair	185	35.00	55.00	30.00
2	Teapot, 4-cup		140	35.00	40.00	20.00

CATS DESIGN, 1992

This design, featuring a cat family, was produced in 1992 for Boots the Chemist.

Backstamp: **A.** Printed "Wade England" with two lines
B. Printed "Cats designed exclusively by Wade" with cats print

No.	Description	Colourways	Size	U.S. $	Can. $	U.K. £
1	Mug, Ver. 1	White; multi-coloured cat print	95	20.00	25.00	12.00
2	Teapot, 4-cup		140	30.00	40.00	20.00

GOOSE FAIR DESIGN, 1991

Backstamp: **A.** Printed "Wade England" with two lines
B. Printed "Goose Fair Designed Exclusively for Boots by Judith Wootton Wade" with two lines

No.	Description	Colourways	Size	U.S. $	Can. $	U.K. £
1	Biscuit barrel, large	White; dark green lid; multi-coloured print of coconut shy/snacks	266	35.00	55.00	30.00
2	Mug, Ver. 2	White; multi-coloured print of a magician	90	20.00	25.00	12.00
3	Teapot, 4-cup	White; dark green lid; multi-coloured print of Peggy Lee Fortune Teller	140	25.00	30.00	15.00

HEDGEROW DESIGN, 1988-1995

The Hedgerow mugs have different animals or birds inside the rim.

Backstamp: Printed "Wade" with two lines

No.	Description	Colourways	Size	U.S. $	Can. $	U.K. £
1a	Mug, Ver. 1	White; orange butterfly inside rim; red poppy flowers; yellow-green grass, leaves	95	10.00	12.00	6.00
1b	Mug, Ver. 1	White; field mouse inside rim; pale blue harebell flowers; yellow green grass, leaves	95	10.00	12.00	6.00
1c	Mug, Ver. 1	White; sparrow inside rim; pale pink campion flowers; yellow green grass, leaves	95	10.00	12.00	6.00
2	Teapot, 6-cup	White; orange butterflies on lid; red/pink/blue flowers; green grass, leaves	165	20.00	30.00	15.00

HERB COLLECTION DESIGN, 1984, 1986-1995

The Herb Collection teapot was first produced in 1984 in a four-cup size. In 1986 a mix and match two-cup teapot, coffee pot, sugar bowl and cream jug were added to complete this breakfast set. For an illustration of this design see page 406.

Photograph of design
not available
at press time

Backstamp: **A.** Printed "Wade" with two lines
B. Printed "Herb Collection Wade England"

No.	Description	Colourways	Size	U.S. $	Can. $	U.K. £
1	Coffee pot	White; grey/pink/green herbs	242	30.00	40.00	25.00
2	Cream jug		95	12.00	16.00	8.00
3	Sugar bowl		65	12.00	16.00	8.00
4	Teapot, 4-cup		140	20.00	30.00	15.00
5	Teapot, 2- cup		115	20.00	30.00	15.00

HOUSE MOUSE DESIGN, 1990-1994

Each of the items is decorated with a different mouse scene.

Backstamp: Embossed "Made in England" printed "Designed exclusively for Boots by Wade Ceramics"

No.	Description	Colourways	Size	U.S. $	Can. $	U.K. £
1	Biscuit barrel, small	White; multi-coloured print	185	25.00	35.00	20.00
2	Cheese dish		100	35.00	40.00	20.00
3	Cream jug		95	12.00	16.00	8.00
4	Mug, Ver. 1		95	10.00	12.00	6.00
5	Sugar bowl		65	12.00	16.00	8.00
6	Teapot, 4-cup		140	20.00	30.00	15.00

LILY DESIGN, 1984, 1986-1995

Photograph of design
not available
at press time

Backstamp: Printed "Wade" with two lines

No.	Description	Colourways	Size	U.S. $	Can. $	U.K. £
1	Mug, Ver. 1	White; pink/mauve flowers; green/grey leaves	95	10.00	12.00	6.00
2	Teapot, 4-cup		140	20.00	30.00	15.00

A
L
B
E
R
T

ORCHARD DESIGN, 1984, 1986-1989

The four-cup Orchard teapot was first produced in 1984. In 1986 a mix and match two-cup teapot, cream jug, sugar bowl and a coffee pot were added to form a breakfast set.

Backstamp: Printed "Orchard Wade England"

No.	Description	Colourways	Size	U.S. $	Can. $	U.K. £
1	Coffee pot	White; brown picket fence; red/green apple tree red flowers	242	30.00	40.00	25.00
2	Cream jug	White; brown picket fence; red flowers	95	12.00	16.00	8.00
3	Sugar bowl	White; brown picket fence; red flowers	65	12.00	16.00	8.00
4	Teapot, 4-cup	White; brown picket fence; red/green apple tree red flowers	140	20.00	30.00	15.00
5	Teapot, 2-cup	White; brown picket fence; red/green apple tree red flowers	115	20.00	30.00	15.00

PANSY DESIGN, 1988-1995

A
L
B
E
R
T

Backstamp: Printed "Wade" with two lines

No.	Description	Colourways	Size	U.S. $	Can. $	U.K. £
1	Mug, Ver. 2	White; deep red/mauve/yellow flowers; grey leaves	90	10.00	12.00	6.00
2	Teapot, 4-cup		140	20.00	30.00	15.00

POPPY DESIGN

The first Albert shaped teapot was produced for Boots the Chemist in 1984 and was available in a six and four-cup size with a matching mug. Between 1988 and 1995 new Poppy design teapots were produced in six-cup and four-cup sizes with matching mugs.

Variation One — Small flowers, 1984

Backstamp: A. Printed half circular "Royal Victoria Pottery Staffordshire Wade England"
B. Printed "Wade England"

No.	Description	Colourways	Size	U.S. $	Can. $	U.K. £
1	Mug, Ver. 1	White; red poppy flowers; green stems	95	10.00	12.00	6.00
2	Teapot, 6-cup		165	30.00	40.00	20.00
3	Teapot, 4-cup		140	35.00	40.00	20.00

Variation Two — Large flowers, 1988-1995

Backstamp: Printed "Wade" with two lines

No.	Description	Colourways	Size	U.S. $	Can. $	U.K. £
1	Mug, Ver. 1	White; red/mauve flowers; green stems and leaves	95	10.00	12.00	6.00
2	Teapot, 6-cup		165	20.00	30.00	15.00
3	Teapot, 4-cup		140	20.00	30.00	15.00

SAMPLER DESIGN, 1988

This teapot has a stitched design of flowers and the word "Teapot" written around the body.

Photograph of design
not available
at press time

Backstamp: Red printed semi-circular "Royal Victoria Pottery Wade England"

No.	Description	Colourways	Size	U.S. $	Can. $	U.K. £
1	Teapot, 4-cup	White; red/green/yellow print	140	20.00	30.00	15.00

VILLAGE SCENES DESIGN, 1988-1995

Photograph of design
not available
at press time

Backstamp: Printed "Wade" with two lines

No.	Description	Colourways	Size	U.S. $	Can. $	U.K. £
1a	Mug, Ver. 1	White; brown and green church scene	95	10.00	12.00	6.00
1b	Mug, Ver. 1	White; brown and green cottage scene	95	10.00	12.00	6.00
2	Teapot, 6-cup	White; brown and green village scene	165	20.00	30.00	15.00

BASKETWARE SHAPE, 1938- c.1960

The Basketware shape encompasses a range of tableware which would be used during light meals such as breakfast or supper. It has an embossed basket weave and flowers design and was produced in a multi-coloured decoration. The butter dish has a recess in the lid for a small butter knife and the biscuit barrel has a cane handle. This popular design was in production for a number of years with new moulds producing variations in size.

VARIATION ONE — MULTI-COLOURED FLOWERS, c.1938 -1939

Available in five colours:

1. Mottled turquoise and orange
2. Pale yellow all over
3. Pale yellow with mauve, purple, yellow flowers
4. White with yellow and blue flowers
5. White pearl with copper lustre squares and maroon/mauve flowers

Cream Jug and Teapot

Fruit Bowl

Biscuit Barrel

Sugar Bowl

Backstamp: **A**. Black ink stamp "Wade Heath England" (round W 1937-c.1940)
           B. Black ink stamp "Made In England" (c.1938-c.1942)
           C. Black ink stamp "Flaxman Wade Heath England" (round W 1937-1940)
           D. Black ink stamp "Noveltio trademark Made in England"
           E. Unmarked

B
A
S
K
E
T
W
A
R
E

1. Mottled Turquoise And Orange Design

No.	Description	Colourways	Size	U.S. $	Can. $	U.K. £
1	Biscuit barrel	Mottled turquoise and orange	165	120.00	150.00	60.00
2	Butter dish		88 x 114	35.00	50.00	25.00
3	Cake plate		240	40.00	45.00	20.00
4	Cheese dish		114	60.00	80.00	45.00
5	Cream jug		80	35.00	45.00	20.00
6	Cruet		65 x 140	65.00	80.00	40.00
7	Fruit bowl		240	55.00	75.00	35.00
8	Pepper		63	18.00	23.00	13.00
9	Preserve jar		130	50.00	60.00	30.00
10	Salt		63	18.00	23.00	13.00
11	Sugar bowl		50	30.00	35.00	15.00
12	Teapot		153	220.00	320.00	160.00

2. Pale Yellow Design

No.	Description	Colourways	Size	U.S. $	Can. $	U.K. £
1	Biscuit barrel	Pale yellow	165	120.00	150.00	60.00
2	Butter dish		88 x 114	35.00	50.00	25.00
3	Cake plate		240	40.00	45.00	20.00
4	Cheese dish		114	60.00	80.00	45.00
5	Cream jug		80	35.00	45.00	20.00
6	Cruet		65 x 140	65.00	80.00	40.00
7	Fruit bowl		240	55.00	75.00	35.00
8	Pepper		63	18.00	23.00	13.00
9	Preserve jar		130	50.00	60.00	30.00
10	Salt		63	18.00	23.00	13.00
11	Sugar bowl		50	30.00	35.00	15.00
12	Teapot		153	220.00	320.00	160.00

3. Pale Yellow With Mauve, Purple, Yellow Flowers Design

No.	Description	Colourways	Size	U.S. $	Can. $	U.K. £
1	Biscuit barrel	Pale yellow; pink/mauve/yellow flowers; green leaves	165	120.00	150.00	60.00
2	Butter dish		88 x 114	35.00	50.00	25.00
3	Cake plate		240	40.00	45.00	20.00
4	Cheese dish		114	60.00	80.00	45.00
5	Cream jug		80	35.00	45.00	20.00
6	Cruet		65 x 140	65.00	80.00	40.00
7	Fruit bowl		240	55.00	75.00	35.00
8	Pepper		63	18.00	23.00	13.00
9	Preserve jar		130	50.00	60.00	30.00
10	Salt		63	18.00	23.00	13.00
11	Sugar bowl		50	30.00	35.00	15.00
12	Teapot		153	220.00	320.00	160.00

4. White With Yellow And Blue Flowers Design

No.	Description	Colourways	Size	U.S. $	Can. $	U.K. £
1	Biscuit barrel	White; yellow/blue flowers; green leaves	165	120.00	150.00	60.00
2	Butter dish		88 x 114	35.00	50.00	25.00
3	Cake plate		240	40.00	45.00	20.00
4	Cheese dish		114	60.00	80.00	45.00
5	Cream jug		80	35.00	45.00	20.00
6	Cruet		65 x 140	65.00	80.00	40.00
7	Fruit bowl		240	55.00	75.00	35.00
8	Pepper		63	18.00	23.00	13.00
9	Preserve jar		130	50.00	60.00	30.00
10	Salt		63	18.00	23.00	13.00
11	Sugar bowl		50	30.00	35.00	15.00
12	Teapot		153	220.00	320.00	160.00

5. White Pearl With Copper Lustre Squares And Maroon/Mauve Flowers Design

No.	Description	Colourways	Size	U.S. $	Can. $	U.K. £
1	Biscuit barrel	White pearl; copper lustre squares; maroon/mauve flowers; green leaves	165	120.00	150.00	60.00
2	Butter dish		88 x 114	35.00	50.00	25.00
3	Cake plate		240	40.00	45.00	20.00
4	Cheese dish		114	60.00	80.00	45.00
5	Cream jug		80	35.00	45.00	20.00
6	Cruet		65 x 140	65.00	80.00	40.00
7	Fruit bowl		240	55.00	75.00	35.00
8	Pepper		63	18.00	23.00	13.00
9	Preserve jar		130	50.00	60.00	30.00
10	Salt		63	18.00	23.00	13.00
11	Sugar bowl		50	30.00	35.00	15.00
12	Teapot		153	220.00	320.00	160.00

BASKETWARE

VARIATION TWO — GOLD FLOWER CHINTZ, c.1953-c.1962

This variation has an all-over gold flower and leaf chintz decoration with hand-painted pink and mauve flowers in the centre. The same gold chintz decoration was also used on a Regency tea set but with transfer printed flowers. The lid on the teapot is ceramic, and the other lids are chrome with clear plastic pink flower finials.

Chrome accent pieces (not produced by Wade) are found on several of the pieces. The biscuit barrel and the honey pot could come with chrome stand and the sandwich plate could have a removable chrome handle. These handles can either be plain or have an embossed design.

Biscuit Barrel with chrome accent   Honey Pot

Backstamp: A. Gold printed semi-circular "Wade made in England Hand Painted" with green ink stamp "A"
B. Gold printed semi-circular "Wade made in England Hand Painted"

No.	Description	Colourways	Size	U.S. $	Can. $	U.K. £
1	Biscuit barrel	White; gold flower/leaf decoration; pink/mauve flowers; green leaves; chrome lid with pink flower; Chrome stand	150 x 125 215 x 150	135.00	175.00	70.00
2	Butter dish	White; gold flower/leaf decoration; pink/mauve flowers; green leaves; chrome lid with pink flower	88 x 114	40.00	45.00	20.00
3	Cake stand, two-tier	White; gold flower/leaf decoration; pink purple flowers; green leaves; chrome handle	229 x 165	35.00	40.00	20.00
4	Cream jug	White; gold flowers/leaf decoration; pink/mauve flowers; green leaves	75	35.00	45.00	25.00
5	Honey pot	White; gold flower/leaf decoration; pink/mauve flowers; green leaves; chrome lid with pink flower; Chrome stand	110 x 95 165 x 125	45.00	60.00	30.00
6	Sandwich plate, oval	White; gold flower/leaf decoration; pink/ purple flowers; green leaves; Chrome handle	285 x 155 235 x 140	55.00	65.00	35.00
7	Sugar bowl	White; gold flower/leaf decoration; pink/mauve flowers; green leaves; chrome lid with pink flower	80 x 110	60.00	80.00	30.00
8	Sugar bowl	White; gold flower/leaf decoration; pink/mauve flowers; green leaves; chrome lid with pink flower; chrome rim and handle	88 x 110	60.00	80.00	30.00
9	Teapot	White; gold flower/leaf decoration; pink/mauve flowers; green leaves	153	95.00	135.00	50.00

B
A
S
K
E
T
W
A
R
E

BEE SHAPE, 1932-c.1940

LARGE LEAVES DESIGN

Backstamp: Orange ink stamp "Wades England" with lion (1927-1933)

No.	Description	Colourways	Size	U.S. $	Can. $	U.K. £
1	Coffee pot	Cream; bright orange leaves; grey flowers; black stems/outline	153	50.00	60.00	30.00
2	Teapot		145	55.00	75.00	35.00

BRAMBLE SHAPE, c.1948 - c.1962

Bramble has an embossed crazy paving background with blackberries (brambles) and leaves. An advertisement of the mid 1950s from a Toronto, Canada, china store, shows the wedge- shaped cheese dish for $1.05, the sauce boat and tray at 95¢ and the salad bowl and servers for $2.55.

Bramble ware has been found in forty- five different shapes and sizes and in fifteen different colour variations. Using the colours and backstamps as a guide, Bramble wares can be divided into four distinct stages.

BRAMBLE WARE SHAPES

Butter dish:	The round butter dish is from the same mould as the large lidded sugar, the butter has a recess in the lid for a small knife.
Cheese dish:	Both an oblong and a wedge shape were produced.
Cruets:	These could be purchased as a salt and pepper or as a set of salt, pepper and mustard pot on a shaped tray.
Dishes:	These were produced in oval and oval with two or four points.
Honey pots	
Jugs:	Milk jugs were produced in six sizes. There are two types of spout.
	Ver. 1 — long spout
	Ver. 2 — short spout.
Odd-shaped bowls:	These bowls have four, five, six and eight points. The four and five point bowls resemble Catherine Wheels and the six and eight points resemble flower heads.
Round bowls:	Seven different size bowls.
Salad bowl and utensils	
Sugar bowls:	Two types and three sizes of sugar bowl were produced.
	Ver. 1 — a wide top and narrow base and in a small size only.
	Ver. 2a — a narrow top and a wide base produced in a medium size without a lid.
	Ver. 2b — a narrow top and a wide base produced in a large size with a lid.
Teapots:	Two types of teapot were produced.
	Ver. 1 — a wide top and narrow base with a blackberry finial.
	Ver. 2 — a narrow top and wide base with a bramble stem finial.

VARIATION 1 — c.1946-c.1948

Bramble wares were first produced in one colour glazes except for white which was also produced with gold highlighting and in a coloured pearlised white.

1. Blush — creamy beige
2. Cane — creamy yellow
3. Emerald green — green of varying shades depending on the thickness of the glaze
4. Lemon — bright yellow
5. Pink
6. Turquoise — blue of varying shades depending on the thickness of the glaze
7. White
8. White gold — White with gold berries and leaves
9. White pearl — Pearlised white with yellow/red/grey berries/leaves

1. Blush Design

Photograph of colourway
not available
at press time

Backstamp: Black ink stamp "Wade England" (c.1948-1950)

No.	Description	Colourways	Size	U.S. $	Can. $	U.K. £
1	Bowl	Creamy beige	101	10.00	15.00	8.00
2	Milk jug, Ver. 2		127	22.00	25.00	12.00
3	Milk jug, Ver. 2		140	22.00	25.00	12.00

2. Cane Design

Photograph of colourway
not available
at press time

Backstamp: Black ink stamp "Wade England" (c.1948-1950)

No.	Description	Colourways	Size	U.S. $	Can. $	U.K. £
1	Milk jug, Ver. 2	Creamy yellow	133	22.00	25.00	12.00

3. Emerald Green Design

Milk Jug, Version One

Backstamp: Black ink stamp "Wade England" (c.1948-1950)

No.	Description	Colourways	Size	U.S. $	Can. $	U.K. £
1	Bowl, four points	Emerald green	150	22.00	30.00	15.00
2	Butter dish		112	35.00	40.00	20.00
3	Cheese dish, wedge shape		88 x 159	45.00	58.00	25.00
4	Cream jug, large		88	22.00	30.00	15.00
5	Cream jug, small		70	18.00	25.00	12.00
6	Cruet		60 x 127	30.00	40.00	20.00
7	Milk jug, Ver. 1		140	25.00	35.00	18.00
8	Pepper		60	10.00	15.00	8.00
9	Salt		60	10.00	15.00	8.00
10	Sugar bowl, Ver. 2a		57	22.00	30.00	15.00
11	Teapot, Ver. 2		153	55.00	70.00	35.00

B R A M B L E

4. *Lemon Design*

Milk Jug, Version Two

Backstamp: Black ink stamp "Wade England" (c.1948-1950)

No.	Description	Colourways	Size	U.S. $	Can. $	U.K. £
1	Milk jug, Ver. 2	Lemon yellow	140	30.00	35.00	15.00

5. *Pink Design*

Photograph of colourway
not available
at press time

Backstamp: Black ink stamp "Wade England" (c.1948-1950)

No.	Description	Colourways	Size	U.S. $	Can. $	U.K. £
1	Cream jug, large	Pink	88	22.00	30.00	15.00
2	Cream jug, small		70	18.00	25.00	12.00
3	Sugar bowl, Ver. 2a		57	22.00	30.00	15.00
4	Teapot, Ver. 1		146	55.00	70.00	35.00

B
R
A
M
B
L
E

6. Turquoise Design

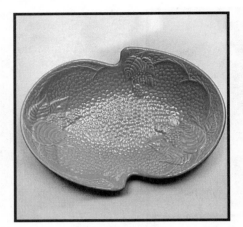

Oval Dish, two points

Milk Jug, Version One

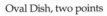

Backstamp: Black ink stamp "Wade England" (c.1948-1950)

No.	Description	Colourways	Size	U.S. $	Can. $	U.K. £
1	Bowl	Turquoise	127	22.00	25.00	12.00
2	Bowl, six points		127	38.00	50.00	25.00
3	Bowl, eight point star		235	40.00	52.00	28.00
4	Butter dish		112	35.00	40.00	20.00
5	Cream jug, large		88	22.00	30.00	15.00
6	Cream jug, small		70	18.00	25.00	12.00
7	Dish, oval, two points		254	20.00	30.00	15.00
8	Dish, oval, two points		305	20.00	30.00	15.00
9	Dish/triple tray		205 x 225	28.00	35.00	16.00
10	Honey pot		114 x 76	25.00	35.00	15.00
11	Milk jug, Ver. 1		146	25.00	35.00	18.00
12	Milk jug, Ver. 2		127	25.00	35.00	18.00
13	Sugar bowl, Ver. 2a		57	15.00	20.00	10.00
14	Teapot, Ver. 1		146	50.00	60.00	30.00
15	Teapot, Ver. 2		153	50.00	60.00	30.00

7. White Design

Photograph of colourway
not available
at press time

Backstamp: Black ink stamp "Wade England" (c.1948-1950)

No.	Description	Colourways	Size	U.S. $	Can. $	U.K. £
1	Cream jug, large	White	88	18.00	25.00	12.00
2	Cream jug, small		70	18.00	25.00	12.00
3	Sugar bowl, Ver. 2a		57	15.00	20.00	10.00
4	Teapot, Ver. 1		146	50.00	60.00	30.00
5	Teapot, Ver. 2		153	50.00	60.00	30.00

B
R
A
M
B
L
E

8. *White Gold Design*

Teapot — Version 1

Cream Jug, Teapot — Version 2, Sugar Bowl — Version 2a

Backstamp: Black ink stamp "Wade England" (c.1948-1950)

No.	Description	Colourways	Size	U.S. $	Can. $	U.K. £
1	Cream jug, large	White; gold berries, leaves	88	20.00	30.00	15.00
2	Sugar bowl, Ver. 2a		57	22.00	30.00	15.00
3	Teapot, Ver. 1		146	60.00	75.00	35.00
4	Teapot, Ver. 2		153	60.00	75.00	35.00

9. *White Pearl Design*

Photograph of colourway
not available
at press time

Backstamp: Black ink stamp "Wade England" (c.1948-1950)

No.	Description	Colourways	Size	U.S. $	Can. $	U.K. £
1	Cream jug, large	White; yellow/red/grey berries, leaves	88	25.00	35.00	18.00
2	Honey pot		114 x 76	25.00	35.00	18.00
3	Sugar bowl, Ver. 2a		57	15.00	20.00	10.00

VARIATION 2 — 1948-1953

The earlier blush coloured (creamy beige) items were enhanced by hand-decorating the berries and leaves in autumn tint colours, bramble colours and gold blush colours. The gold blush design name was added to the backstamp in gold.

1. Autumn tints — creamy beige with orange/yellow/brown/grey berries and leaves.
2. Natural bramble — creamy beige with deep red/purple berries and green leaves.
3. Gold blush — creamy beige with rose red and gold berries and leaves.

1. Autumn Tints Design

Cheese dish, oblong

Sugar Bowl — Version 2

Backstamp: Black ink stamp "Wade Bramble England" (1948-1953)

No.	Description	Colourways	Size	U.S. $	Can. $	U.K. £
1	Bowl	Creamy beige with orange/yellow/brown/grey berries and leaves	101	10.00	15.00	8.00
2	Bowl		127	10.00	15.00	8.00
3	Bowl		153	12.00	15.00	8.00
4	Bowl		177	15.00	20.00	10.00
5	Bowl		205	35.00	40.00	20.00
6	Bowl		229	35.00	40.00	20.00
7	Butter dish		95 x 112	35.00	40.00	20.00
8	Cheese dish, oblong		75 x 140	55.00	70.00	35.00
9	Cream jug, small		70	18.00	25.00	12.00
10	Cream jug, large		88	20.00	25.00	12.00
11	Cruet		111 x 127	45.00	55.00	25.00
12	Dish, oval		205	25.00	35.00	18.00
13	Dish, oval		254	25.00	35.00	18.00
14	Dish, oval		305	30.00	40.00	20.00
15	Honey pot		114 x 76	38.00	50.00	15.00
16	Milk jug, Ver. 1		114	25.00	35.00	18.00
17	Milk jug, Ver. 1		133	35.00	40.00	20.00
18	Milk jug, Ver. 1		140	35.00	40.00	20.00
19	Milk jug, Ver. 1		146	35.00	40.00	20.00
20	Pepper		60	10.00	15.00	8.00
21	Salad bowl		101 x 165	45.00	55.00	30.00
22	Salad servers		210	30.00	40.00	20.00
23	Salt		60	10.00	15.00	8.00
24	Sugar bowl, Ver. 1		44 x 76	18.00	22.00	12.00
25	Sugar bowl, Ver. 2a		57	18.00	22.00	12.00
26	Sugar bowl, Ver. 2b		95	28.00	35.00	18.00
27	Teapot, Ver. 2		153	55.00	60.00	30.00

BRAMBLE

2. *Bramble Design*

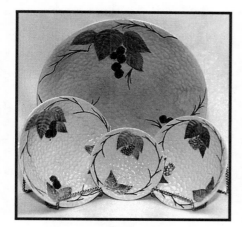

Bowls

Cruet

Backstamp: Black ink stamp "Wade Bramble England" (1948-1953)

No.	Description	Colourways	Size	U.S. $	Can. $	U.K. £
1	Bowl	Creamy beige with deep red/purple/ berries; green leaves	101	15.00	20.00	10.00
2	Bowl		127	15.00	20.00	10.00
3	Bowl		153	20.00	25.00	15.00
4	Bowl		177	35.00	40.00	20.00
5	Bowl		205	35.00	40.00	20.00
6	Bowl		229	35.00	40.00	20.00
7	Bowl		242	35.00	40.00	20.00
8	Butter dish		95 x 112	35.00	40.00	20.00
9	Cheese dish, oblong		75 x 140	35.00	40.00	20.00
10	Cheese dish, wedge		88 x 159	45.00	58.00	25.00
11	Cream jug, small		70	18.00	25.00	12.00
12	Cream jug, large		88	25.00	32.00	18.00
13	Cruet		53 x 111	45.00	55.00	25.00
14	Dish, oval		205	25.00	35.00	18.00
15	Dish, oval		254	35.00	40.00	20.00
16	Dish, oval		305	35.00	40.00	20.00
17	Dish, triple tray		225	35.00	45.00	28.00
18	Honey pot		114 x 76	35.00	45.00	25.00
19	Milk jug, Ver. 1		114	25.00	32.00	18.00
20	Milk jug, Ver. 1		133	35.00	40.00	20.00
21	Milk jug, Ver. 1		140	35.00	40.00	20.00
22	Milk jug, Ver. 1		146	35.00	45.00	30.00
23	Pepper		60	10.00	15.00	8.00
24	Salad bowl		101 x 165	55.00	70.00	35.00
25	Salad servers		210	25.00	35.00	18.00
26	Salt		60	10.00	15.00	8.00
27	Sauce boat/tray		63 x 155	28.00	38.00	18.00
28	Sugar bowl, Ver. 1		44	18.00	22.00	10.00
29	Sugar bowl, Ver. 2a		57	18.00	22.00	10.00
30	Sugar bowl, Ver. 2b		95	35.00	40.00	20.00
31	Teapot, Ver. 2		153	60.00	70.00	35.00

3. *Gold Blush Design*

Bowl, four points   Dish/triple tray

Backstamp: Black ink stamp "Wade Bramble England" (1948-1953) design name in gold

No.	Description	Colourways	Size	U.S. $	Can. $	U.K. £
1	Bowl, four points	Creamy beige; rose red/gold berries, leaves	150	35.00	40.00	20.00
2	Cheese dish, wedge		88 x 159	45.00	58.00	25.00
3	Cream jug, large		88	25.00	35.00	18.00
4	Dish/triple tray		225	35.00	40.00	20.00
5	Milk jug, Ver. 1		133	35.00	40.00	20.00
6	Milk jug, Ver. 1		140	35.00	40.00	20.00
7	Sugar bowl, Ver. 2a		57	20.00	25.00	12.00
8	Sugar bowl, Ver. 2b		95	28.00	35.00	18.00
9	Teapot, Ver. 2		153	75.00	100.00	50.00

BRAMBLE

VARIATION 3 — 1953- c.1962

In 1953 new life was given to unsold one colour glazed items by highlighting them with gold. These revived items can be identified by their double backstamps. These gold highlighted Bramble wares were an immediate success and were produced from 1953 until the early 1960s.

1. Emerald gold — Emerald green with gold berries and leaves.
2. Golden turquoise — Turquoise blue with gold berries and leaves.

1. Emerald Gold Design

Bowls

Salad Bowl and Servers

Backstamp: Gold transfer printed "Wade England" with the design name included stamped over or next to the original black ink stamp "Wade England"

No.	Description	Colourways	Size	U.S. $	Can. $	U.K. £
1	Bowl	Emerald green; gold berries, leaves	101	12.00	18.00	10.00
2	Bowl		153	15.00	20.00	10.00
3	Bowl		177	15.00	20.00	10.00
4	Bowl, round, four points		150	20.00	25.00	12.00
5	Butter dish		95 x 112	35.00	40.00	20.00
6	Cheese dish, wedge		88 x 159	45.00	58.00	25.00
7	Cream jug, small		111 x 127	15.00	20.00	10.00
8	Cruet		53	35.00	40.00	20.00
9	Dish, oval, two points		254	28.00	40.00	20.00
10	Dish, oval, two points		300	28.00	40.00	20.00
11	Dish, oval, four points		205	30.00	40.00	22.00
12	Dish/triple tray		225	35.00	40.00	20.00
13	Honey pot		114	35.00	40.00	20.00
14	Milk jug, Ver. 1		127	35.00	40.00	20.00
15	Pepper		60	10.00	15.00	8.00
16	Salad bowl		101 x 165	45.00	60.00	30.00
17	Salad servers		210	24.00	30.00	16.00
18	Salt		60	10.00	15.00	8.00
19	Sauce boat/tray		63 x 155	28.00	38.00	18.00
20	Sugar bowl, Ver. 1		40	18.00	22.00	12.00

3. Golden Turquoise Design

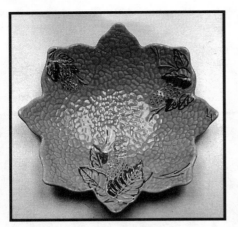

Bowl, eight points

Milk Jug, Version One

Backstamp: Gold transfer printed "Wade England" with the design name included stamped over or next to the original black ink stamp "Wade England"

No.	Description	Colourways	Size	U.S. $	Can. $	U.K. £
1	Bowl	Turquoise blue; gold berries, leaves	127	18.00	22.00	12.00
2	Bowl, six points		127	38.00	50.00	25.00
3	Bowl, eight points		235	25.00	35.00	15.00
4	Butter dish		95 x 112	35.00	40.00	20.00
5	Cream jug, large		88	20.00	30.00	15.00
6	Cream jug, small		70	15.00	20.00	10.00
7	Dish, oval, two points		254	28.00	40.00	20.00
8	Dish, oval, two points		305	28.00	40.00	20.00
9	Dish/triple tray		205 x 225	18.00	25.00	12.00
10	Milk jug, Ver. 1		159	28.00	38.00	18.00
11	Pepper		60	10.00	15.00	8.00
12	Salt		60	10.00	15.00	8.00
13	Sugar bowl, Ver. 1		44	18.00	22.00	12.00
14	Sugar bowl, Ver. 2a		57	18.00	22.00	12.00
15	Sugar bowl, Ver. 2b		95	22.00	30.00	15.00
16	Teapot, Ver. 1		146	75.00	100.00	50.00
17	Teapot, Ver. 2		153	75.00	100.00	50.00

B
R
A
M
B
L
E

VARIATION 4 — c.1955

Black Velvet — Black with gold berries and leaves.

Black Velvet Design

Sugar Bowl, Version 2b (without lid)

Cheese Dish

B
R
A
M
B
L
E

Backstamp: Gold transfer printed "Black Velvet Wade Made in England hand-painted"

No.	Description	Colourways	Size	U.S. $	Can. $	U.K. £
1	Cheese dish	Black; gold berries, leaves	88 x 159	45.00	58.00	25.00
2	Cream jug, large		88	35.00	45.00	22.00
3	Cruet		111 x 127	60.00	90.00	30.00
4	Milk jug, Ver. 1		133	35.00	45.00	22.00
5	Pepper		60	15.00	20.00	10.00
6	Salad bowl		101 x 165	40.00	55.00	28.00
7	Salad severs		210	25.00	30.00	15.00
9	Salt		60	15.00	20.00	10.00
10	Sauce boat/tray		63 x 155	38.00	50.00	25.00
11	Sugar bowl, Ver. 2b		95	35.00	40.00	20.00
12	Teapot, Ver. 2		153	60.00	80.00	40.00

CLIFTON SHAPE, 1927-1933

This decagonal (ten-sided) teapot is similar to the Canton shape teapot (see page 204), but the straight top handle has a curved side. The lid sits inside the neck of the teapot and has an acorn-shaped finial.

Backstamp: **A.** Orange ink stamp "Wades England" with lion (1927-1933)
B. Black ink stamp "Wadeheath England" with lion (1933-1937)

No.	Description	Colourways	Size	U.S. $	Can. $	U.K. £
1	Hot water jug	Cream; yellow/orange/blue flowers; green leaves; orange/black wavy line	195	60.00	80.00	40.00
2	Teapot, 6-cup	Cream; yellow/orange/blue flowers; green leaves; orange/black wavy line	165	65.00	85.00	45.00
3a	Teapot, 4-cup	Cream pot; floral wavy bands	159	65.00	85.00	45.00
3b	Teapot, 4-cup	Cream pot; multi-coloured cottage and garden print	159	55.00	70.00	35.00
3c	Teapot, 4-cup	Cream pot; multi-coloured floral band	159	60.00	70.00	35.00

CLOWN SHAPE, 1992-1993

Bow and Kipper Mug

Bow Teapot

Kipper Teapot

Backstamp: Printed "Wade England" with two lines

No.	Description	Colourways	Size	U.S. $	Can. $	U.K. £
1	Bowl	White; multi-coloured print of Bow and Kipper clowns and balloons	171	10.00	15.00	8.00
2	Egg cup	White; multi-coloured print of Bow and Kipper clowns and balloons	44	8.00	10.00	3.00
3	Mug	White; multi-coloured print of Bow and Kipper clowns and balloons	70	10.00	15.00	8.00
4	Plate	White; multi-coloured print of Bow and Kipper clowns and balloons	190	12.00	15.00	8.00
5	Teapot	White; green/red striped bow-tie, yellow hair, shoes	184	35.00	40.00	20.00
6	Teapot	White; green/red spotted tie, yellow hair; blue shoes	200	35.00	40.00	20.00

COMPACTO SHAPE

STYLE ONE — 1927-1933

The lid of Style One teapots is level with the top and the handle is curved.

FLOWERED DESIGN

Backstamp: Embossed "Wades" and ink stamp "England Wades" with registration number

No.	Description	Colourways	Size	U.S. $	Can. $	U.K. £
1	Teapot	White; large orange/blue flowers; green leaves; blue/ orange dots in leaf	108	80.00	100.00	50.00

GOLD WREATH DESIGN

Backstamp: Embossed "Wades Made in England" red ink stamp "Wades Compacto, Teapot" with registration number

No.	Description	Colourways	Size	U.S. $	Can. $	U.K. £
1	Teapot	Dark green; gold decoration; white beaded garland; pale blue flowers/beads	108	80.00	100.00	50.00

PAISLEY DESIGN

The popular Paisley chintz print was used by many other potteries

Backstamp: Orange ink stamp "Wades England Compacto" with lion

No.	Description	Colourways	Size	U.S. $	Can. $	U.K. £
1	Hot water jug	White; multi-coloured paisley design	108	175.00	200.00	100.00
2	Teapot		108	175.00	200.00	100.00

STYLE TWO — 1927-1933

Style Two pieces have raised lids with a loop finial and angled handles and a straight body.

FLORAL PRINT ON RIM DESIGN

COMPACTO

Backstamp: Orange ink stamp "Wades England" with lion

No.	Description	Colourways	Size	U.S. $	Can. $	U.K. £
1	Hot water jug	Orange; multi-coloured flowers print on rim	135 x 200	80.00	105.00	55.00
2	Teapot		135 x 235	80.00	105.00	55.00
3	Tray		180 x 205	35.00	40.00	20.00
—	Set			225.00	275.00	150.00

HAND-PAINTED DESIGN

Backstamp: Orange ink stamp "Wades England"

No.	Description	Colourways	Size	U.S. $	Can. $	U.K. £
1	Hot water jug	Black; gold edging/trellis decoration; orange flowers	135 x 200	80.00	105.00	55.00
2	Teapot		135 x 235	80.00	105.00	55.00
3	Tray		180 x 205	35.00	40.00	20.00
—	Set			225.00	275.00	150.00

SOLID COLOURS DESIGN

Photograph of design
not available
at press time

Backstamp: Orange ink stamp "Wades England" with lion and embossed "British"

No.	Description	Colourways	Size	U.S. $	Can. $	U.K. £
1a	Hot water jug	Brown; gold edging	135 x 200	60.00	90.00	45.00
2a	Teapot		135 x 200	60.00	90.00	45.00
3a	Tray		180 x 205	20.00	30.00	15.00
—	Set			175.00	250.00	125.00
1b	Hot water jug	Dark green; gold edging	135 x 200	60.00	90.00	45.00
2b	Teapot		135 x 200	60.00	90.00	45.00
3b	Tray		180 x 205	20.00	30.00	15.00
—	Set			175.00	250.00	125.00

C O M P A C T O

MARBLED AND STREAKED COLOURS DESIGN

Backstamp: Orange ink stamp "Wades England" with lion and embossed "British"

No.	Description	Colourways	Size	U.S. $	Can. $	U.K. £
1a	Hot water jug	Marbled blue/brown; gold edging	135 x 200	75.00	100.00	50.00
2a	Teapot		135 x 235	75.00	100.00	50.00
3a	Tray		180 x 205	20.00	30.00	15.00
—	Set			200.00	250.00	125.00
1b	Hot water jug	Marbled brown; gold edging	135 x 200	75.00	100.00	50.00
2b	Teapot		135 x 235	75.00	100.00	50.00
3b	Tray		180 x 205	20.00	30.00	15.00
—	Set			200.00	250.00	125.00
1c	Hot water jug	Marbled cobalt blue/blue; gold edging	135 x 200	75.00	100.00	50.00
2c	Teapot		135 x 235	75.00	100.00	50.00
3c	Tray		180 x 205	20.00	30.00	15.00
—	Set			200.00	250.00	125.00
1d	Hot water jug	Marbled red/orange; gold edging	135 x 200	75.00	100.00	50.00
2d	Teapot		135 x 235	75.00	100.00	50.00
3d	Tray		180 x 205	20.00	30.00	15.00
—	Set			200.00	250.00	125.00
1e	Hot water Jug	Yellow/green streaks; gold edging	135 x 200	85.00	120.00	65.00
2e	Teapot		135 x 235	85.00	120.00	65.00
3e	Tray		180 x 205	25.00	35.00	20.00
—	Set			225.00	300.00	175.00

PAISLEY DESIGN

The very popular paisley chintz print is in multiple blue/yellow/orange and green colours.

See page 29 for
an illustration
of this design

Backstamp: Orange ink stamp "Wades England" with lion

No.	Description	Colourways	Size	U.S. $	Can. $	U.K. £
1	Hot water jug	White; multi-coloured paisley print	135 x 200	175.00	200.00	100.00
2	Teapot		135 x 235	175.00	200.00	100.00
3	Tray		180 x 205	65.00	80.00	40.00
—	Set			450.00	550.00	275.00

COTTAGE SHAPE, 1934-1937

The Cottage combination tea/supper set is shaped as a beamed and thatched cottage with an embossed decoration of small flowers. To differentiate between the butter dish and the cheese dish look at the base. The butter has a "boxed" base and the cheese has a flat base. A similar cottage set was issued in 1937 with some changes in the design and named Fairy Cottage (see page 54). Cottage and Fairy Cottage can be distinguished by the windows, which are square lattice on Cottage pieces and diamond lattice on Fairy Cottage pieces.

Backstamp: Black ink stamp "Wadeheath England" with lion

No.	Description	Colourways	Size	U.S. $	Can. $	U.K. £
1a	Biscuit barrel	Blue	140	120.00	170.00	85.00
1b	Biscuit barrel	Green	140	120.00	170.00	85.00
1c	Biscuit barrel	Cream cottage; yellow/brown thatched roof; brown chimney, door, mushrooms; grey beams, door and window frames maroon/yellow/dark blue flowers;	140	225.00	270.00	135.00
1d	Biscuit barrel	Cream cottage; yellow/brown thatched roof; brown chimney beams, door, windows mushrooms; maroon/yellow/blue flowers	140	225.00	270.00	135.00
2a	Butter dish	Cream cottage; light green base and leaves; light brown tree, roof, beams, window, door; light blue/pink/yellow flowers	120 x 180	225.00	270.00	135.00
2b	Butter dish	Cream cottage/dark green base and leaves; dark brown roof, beams, door; dark blue/orange/yellow flowers	120 x 180	225.00	270.00	135.00
3a	Cheese dish	Beige	120 x 180	135.00	180.00	95.00
3b	Cheese dish	Dark blue	120 x 180	135.00	180.00	95.00
3c	Cheese dish	Pale blue	120 x 180	135.00	180.00	95.00
3d	Cheese dish	Pale green	120 x 180	135.00	180.00	95.00
3e	Cheese dish	Orange	120 x 180	135.00	180.00	95.00
4	Cream jug	Pale blue	70	50.00	65.00	35.00
5a	Honey/jam pot	Cream cottage; yellow/brown roof; grey beams/door/windows	76	65.00	85.00	45.00
5b	Honey/jam pot	Pale blue	76	55.00	70.00	35.00
6a	Teapot	Blue	159	135.00	180.00	95.00
6b	Teapot	Cream cottage; yellow roof, grey/yellow chimney; grey beams/door and window frames; brown door/ mushrooms; small maroon/yellow/blue flowers	159	225.00	270.00	135.00
6c	Teapot	Cream cottage; brown roof, red/brown chimney; brown beams/door and window frames; brown door/mushrooms; maroon/yellow/blue flowers	159	225.00	270.00	135.00

DANDY SHAPE, c.1938 -c1962

A jug and sugar bowl were produced in the Dandy shape and a Nelson shaped teapot was often used to make a three-piece set. The jugs were produced in six sizes. There are slight variations in the handle where it joins at the neck, on the cream jugs there is only a thumb rest on the top of the handle, on the larger and heavier milk jugs there is a thumb rest and a finger grip projection underneath. Due to Dandy's long production run, there are size variations resulting from mould renewals. Some of the designs used on Dandy items were also used on Dutch jugs, Flair sugar and Nelson teapots. As no design names have been found for the hand-painted flower designs, we have named them after the flowers they resemble for ease of reference.

There are four decorative variations:

D A N D Y

1. Copper lustre all over
2. Copper lustre with hand-painted decoration on top
3a. Cream or coloured background with hand-painted decoration, with copper lustre highlights
3b. Cream or coloured background with hand-painted decoration, without copper lustre highlights
4a. White background with transfer prints, with copper lustre highlights
4b. White background with transfer prints, without copper lustre highlights

VARIATION 1   COPPER LUSTRE ALL OVER

Copper Lustre Design

Backstamp: Green ink stamp "Harvest Ware Wade England" (c.1948-c.1952)

No.	Description	Colourways	Size	U.S. $	Can. $	U.K. £
1	Cream jug, large	Copper	90	20.00	25.00	12.00
2	Cream jug, small		75	20.00	25.00	12.00
3	Milk jug, extra large		160	40.00	55.00	30.00
4	Milk jug, large		145	35.00	45.00	25.00
5	Milk jug, medium		130	35.00	45.00	25.00
6	Milk jug, small		115	25.00	35.00	15.00
7	Sugar bowl, small		35	20.00	25.00	12.00

VARIATION 2   COPPER LUSTRE WITH HAND-PAINTED DESIGNS

Aster Design

D
A
N
D
Y

Backstamp: A. Green ink stamp "Wade England" (crossed W c.1948)
B. Gold printed semi-circular "Wade Made in England Hand Painted" (1953-1961)

No.	Description	Colourways	Size	U.S. $	Can. $	U.K. £
1	Cream jug, large	Copper; pink aster flowers; yellow-green leaves	90	25.00	30.00	15.00
2	Milk jug, large		145	30.00	35.00	18.00
3	Sugar bowl, large		50	18.00	20.00	10.00

Clover Design

Backstamp: A. Green ink stamp "Wade England" (crossed W c.1947)
B. Green ink stamp "Harvest Ware Wade England" (c.1948-c.1952)

No.	Description	Colourways	Size	U.S. $	Can. $	U.K. £
1	Cream jug, large	Copper; pink/yellow/green clover and leaves	90	25.00	35.00	18.00
2	Cream jug, small		75	20.00	30.00	15.00
3	Milk jug, small		115	25.00	35.00	18.00
4	Sugar bowl, large		50	20.00	25.00	12.00
5	Sugar bowl, small		35	20.00	25.00	12.00

Crocus Design

A brightly coloured hand-painted design of crocus flowers on copper.

Photograph of design
not available
at press time

Backstamp: Green ink stamp "Harvest Ware Wade England" (c.1948-c.1952)

No.	Description	Colourways	Size	U.S. $	Can. $	U.K. £
1	Cream jug, large	Copper lustre; yellow green leaves; large pink/ yellow crocus flowers	90	25.00	35.00	15.00
2	Sugar bowl, large		50	20.00	25.00	12.00

Georgian Oak Design

This design is of large hand-painted oak leaves with acorns on copper.

For an illustration
of this design see
page 213

Backstamp: **A.** Green ink stamp "Wade Heath England" (round W) 1937-1940
B. Green ink stamp "Wade England" (crossed W c.1947)

No.	Description	Colourways	Size	U.S. $	Can. $	U.K. £
1	Cream jug, large	Copper lustre; white oak leaves and acorns	90	25.00	35.00	15.00
2	Cream jug, small		75	20.00	22.00	12.00
3	Milk jug, extra large		160	35.00	40.00	20.00
4	Milk jug, small		115	35.00	40.00	20.00
5	Sugar bowl, large		50	20.00	25.00	12.00
6	Sugar bowl, small		35	20.00	25.00	12.00

Phlox Design

Backstamp A. Green ink stamp "Harvest Ware Wade England" (c.1948-c.1952)
B. Gold printed semi-circular "Wade Made in England hand-painted" (1953-1961)

No.	Description	Colourways	Size	U.S. $	Can. $	U.K. £
1	Cream jug, large	Copper; grey green leaves; small pink flowers	90	25.00	35.00	15.00
2	Cream jug, small		75	20.00	22.00	12.00
3	Sugar bowl, large		50	20.00	25.00	12.00

VARIATION 3A   CREAM OR WHITE BACKGROUND WITH HANDPAINTED DESIGNS, WITH COPPER LUSTRE HIGHLIGHTS

Banded Design

The bands have hand-painted flowers and leaves.

Photograph of design
not available
at press time

Backstamp: **A.** Green ink stamp "Wade Heath England" (round W 1937-1940)
B. Silver printed "Wade made in England Hand Painted" (1953)

No.	Description	Colourways	Size	U.S. $	Can. $	U.K. £
1	Cream jug, large	Cream; copper; pale green band; green fern leaves; small pink flowers	90	25.00	35.00	15.00
2	Sugar bowl, large		50	20.00	25.00	12.00

Copper Leaves Design

There are two different copper leaf designs.

Variation One — Leaves and Flowers

Backstamp: Green ink stamp "Wade Heath England" (round W 1937-1940)

No.	Description	Colourways	Size	U.S. $	Can. $	U.K. £
1	Cream jug, small	White; copper trim, leaves	75	20.00	25.00	12.00
2	Sugar bowl, small		35	20.00	25.00	12.00

D
A
N
D
Y

Variation Two — Oak leaf and berries

D
A
N
D
Y

Backstamp: Green ink stamp "Wade England A" (c.1945)

No.	Description	Colourways	Size	U.S. $	Can. $	U.K. £
1	Cream jug, small	White; copper trim, leaves, berries	75	22.00	25.00	12.00
2	Milk jug, small		115	22.00	25.00	12.00
3	Sugar bowl, small		35	20.00	25.00	12.00

Cranberry Design

Backstamp: A. Green ink stamp "Wade England" (crossed W c.1947)
B. Green ink stamp "Harvest Ware Wade England" (c.1948-c.1952)

No.	Description	Colourways	Size	U.S. $	Can. $	U.K. £
1	Cream jug, small	White; copper trim; green/yellow leaves; red cranberries	75	20.00	30.00	12.00
2	Milk jug, extra large		160	35.00	40.00	20.00
3	Sugar bowl, small		35	20.00	25.00	12.00

Dahlia Design

Backstamp: Green ink stamp "Harvest Ware Wade England" (c.1948-c.1952)

No.	Description	Colourways	Size	U.S. $	Can. $	U.K. £
1	Milk jug, medium	White; copper trim; maroon/yellow flowers; green/brown leaves	130	35.00	45.00	22.00

Daisies Design

Variation One — Heart-shaped petals

Backstamp: Green ink stamp "Wade Heath England" (round W 1937-1940)

No.	Description	Colourways	Size	U.S. $	Can. $	U.K. £
1	Milk jug, extra large	Cream; copper trim; large maroon/purple flowers; green/brown leaves	160	40.00	55.00	25.00

DANDY

Variation Two — Pointed petals

For an illustration
of this design
see page 312

Backstamp: Green ink stamp "Wade Heath England" (round W 1937-1940)

No.	Description	Colourways	Size	U.S. $	Can. $	U.K. £
1	Cream jug, large	Copper trim; small mauve/maroon flowers; green/orange leaves	90	25.00	35.00	15.00
2	Cream jug, small		75	25.00	35.00	15.00
3	Sugar bowl, large		50	20.00	25.00	12.00

Variation Three — Round petals

For an illustration
of this design
see page 312

Backstamp: Green ink stamp "Wade Heath England" (round W 1937-1940)

No.	Description	Colourways	Size	U.S. $	Can. $	U.K. £
1	Cream jug, small	Copper trim; large maroon/purple flowers; green/brown leaves	75	25.00	30.00	15.00
2	Milk jug, small		115	25.00	35.00	18.00
3	Sugar bowl, small		35	22.00	28.00	14.00

Georgian Design

Backstamp: Green ink stamp "Wade Heath England" (round W 1937-1940)

No.	Description	Colourways	Size	U.S. $	Can. $	U.K. £
1	Milk jug, large	White; copper trim, flower heads, leaves	145	30.00	40.00	20.00
2	Milk jug, medium		130	30.00	40.00	20.00

DANDY

Honeysuckle Design

For an illustration
of this design
see page 313

Backstamp: Green ink stamp "Wade England" (crossed W c.1947)

No.	Description	Colourways	Size	U.S. $	Can. $	U.K. £
1	Milk jug, extra large	Copper trim; pink honeysuckle flowers; green leaves	160	40.00	55.00	25.00

Peonies Design

Hand-painted peony flowers are one of Wades most popular designs and are found on many decorative vases and jugs.

Backstamp: Green ink stamp "Harvest Ware Wade England" (c.1948-c.1952)

No.	Description	Colourways	Size	U.S. $	Can. $	U.K. £
1	Cream jug, large	Cream; copper trim; purple/yellow flowers; green leaves	90	30.00	40.00	20.00
2	Cream jug, small	Cream; copper trim; large maroon/yellow flowers; green leaves	75	25.00	35.00	18.00
3	Sugar bowl, small	Cream; copper trim; purple/yellow flowers; green leaves	35	25.00	35.00	18.00

DANDY

Plums Design

Backstamp: **A.** Green ink stamp "Wade England" (crossed W c.1945-c.1948)
B. Green ink stamp "Harvest Ware Wade England" (c.1948-c.1952)

No.	Description	Colourways	Size	U.S. $	Can. $	U.K. £
1	Cream jug, large	White; copper trim; maroon/purple plums; dark green/brown leaves	90	35.00	45.00	22.00
2	Cream jug, small		75	25.00	35.00	18.00
3	Milk jug, extra large		160	45.00	60.00	30.00
4	Milk jug, large		145	40.00	50.00	25.00
5	Milk jug, medium		130	40.00	50.00	25.00
6	Sugar bowl, small		35	20.00	25.00	16.00

Poppy Design

Backstamp: **A.** Green ink stamp "Wade England" (crossed W c.1947)
B. Green ink stamp "Harvest Ware Wade England" (c.1948-c.1952)

No.	Description	Colourways	Size	U.S. $	Can. $	U.K. £
1	Cream jug, large	Cream; copper trim; maroon/mauve flowers; green/brown leaves	90	25.00	35.00	18.00
2	Cream jug, small		75	25.00	35.00	18.00
3	Milk jug, medium		130	35.00	45.00	22.00

DANDY

Roses Design

Backstamp: **A.** Green ink stamp "Wade Heath England" (round W 1937-1940)
B. Green ink stamp "Wade England" (crossed W c.1947)
C. Silver printed "Wade made in England hand-painted" (1953)

No.	Description	Colourways	Size	U.S. $	Can. $	U.K. £
1	Cream jug, small	Green; copper trim; dark green band; pink rose	75	20.00	25.00	12.00
2	Milk jug, large		145	30.00	40.00	20.00

Vines Design

Four types of hand-painted vine leaves are known

Variation One —Vine with two pointed copper leaves

Backstamp: Unknown

No.	Description	Colourways	Size	U.S. $	Can. $	U.K. £
1	Sugar bowl, large	Dark blue; copper bands, vine/leaves	50	20.00	25.00	12.00

D
A
N
D
Y

Variation Two — Vine with three serrated leaves and berries

Backstamp: Green ink stamp "Harvest Ware Wade England" (c.1948–c.1952)

No.	Description	Colourways	Size	U.S. $	Can. $	U.K. £
1	Milk jug, medium	Cream; copper trim; dark green leaves/berries	130	35.00	45.00	22.00

Variation Three — Vine with five large pointed leaves and berries

Photograph of design
not available
at press time

Backstamp: Green ink stamp "Harvest Ware Wade England" (c.1948–c.1952)

No.	Description	Colourways	Size	U.S. $	Can. $	U.K. £
1	Milk jug, extra large	Cream; copper trim; green/yellow leaves; red berries	160	35.00	40.00	20.00

DANDY

Variation Four — Vine with five large serrated leaves and berries

Backstamp: Green ink stamp "Harvest Ware Wade England" (c.1948-c.1952)

No.	Description	Colourways	Size	U.S. $	Can. $	U.K. £
1	Cream jug, small	Cream; copper trim; green/yellow vine leaves; red berries	75	20.00	30.00	12.00
2	Milk jug, medium		130	35.00	40.00	22.00
3	Sugar bowl, small		35	20.00	25.00	12.00

VARIATION 3B   CREAM OR COLOURED BACKGROUND WITH HANDPAINTED DESIGNS, WITHOUT COPPER LUSTRE HIGHLIGHTS

Banded Design

The bands have hand-painted flowers and leaves.

Photograph of design
not available
at press time

Backstamp: **A.** Green ink stamp "Wade Heath England" (round W 1937-1940)
B. Silver printed "Wade made in England Hand Painted" (1953)

No.	Description	Colourways	Size	U.S. $	Can. $	U.K. £
1	Cream jug, large	White; silver and pink bands; pink flowers; green leaves; silver dots and curved lines	90	25.00	35.00	15.00

D
A
N
D
Y

Blossoms Design

D
A
N
D
Y

Backstamp: Green ink stamp "Wade England A" (c.1945)

No.	Description	Colourways	Size	U.S. $	Can. $	U.K. £
1	Cream jug, large	White; green/orange flowers; grey leaves	90	20.00	30.00	15.00

Daisies Design

Backstamp: Green ink stamp "Wade Heath England" (round W 1937-1940)

No.	Description	Colourways	Size	U.S. $	Can. $	U.K. £
1	Milk jug, large	Cream; pale green bands; small maroon/yellow/ mauve flowers; green/brown leaves	145	22.00	35.00	18.00
2	Milk jug, small		115	22.00	35.00	18.00

Fuschia Design

This beautiful hand-painted design is of Fuschia Fulgens, a variety of fuschia.

Photograph of design
not available
at press time

Backstamp: Green ink stamp "Wade Heath England" (round W 1937-1940)

No.	Description	Colourways	Size	U.S. $	Can. $	U.K. £
1	Milk jug, large	Cream; red/yellow fuschias; green leaves	145	25.00	40.00	20.00

Peonies Design

Backstamp: Green ink stamp "Harvest Ware Wade England" (c.1948-c.1952)

No.	Description	Colourways	Size	U.S. $	Can. $	U.K. £
1	Cream jug, large	Cream; purple/yellow flowers; green/brown leaves	90	30.00	40.00	20.00
2	Milk jug, extra large	Cream; purple/yellow flower; green/brown leaves	160	40.00	55.00	25.00
3	Sugar bowl, large	Cream; maroon/mauve flowers; green/brown leaves	50	25.00	35.00	18.00

D A N D Y

Poppy Design

For an illustration
of this design
see page 42

Backstamp: **A.** Green ink stamp "Wade England" (crossed W c.1947)
B. Green ink stamp "Harvest Ware Wade England" (c.1948-c.1952)

No.	Description	Colourways	Size	U.S. $	Can. $	U.K. £
1	Cream jug, small	Cream; maroon/mauve flowers; green/brown leaves	75	25.00	35.00	18.00
2	Sugar bowl, large		50	25.00	35.00	18.00
3	Sugar bowl, small		35	25.00	35.00	18.00

Roses Design

For an illustration
of this design
see page 43

Backstamp: **A.** Green ink stamp "Wade Heath England" (round W 1937-1940)
B. Green ink stamp "Wade England" (crossed W c.1947)
C. Silver printed "Wade made in England hand-painted" (1953)

No.	Description	Colourways	Size	U.S. $	Can. $	U.K. £
1	Cream jug, large	Green; pink rose	90	25.00	35.00	15.00

D
A
N
D
Y

Splash Design

Backstamp: Green ink stamp "Wade England A" (c.1945)

No.	Description	Colourways	Size	U.S. $	Can. $	U.K. £
1	Milk jug, small	White; grey bands; brown/green splashes	115	15.00	20.00	12.00

VARIATION 4A   WHITE BACKGROUND WITH TRANSFER PRINTS, WITH COPPER LUSTRE HIGHLIGHTS

Blue Daisy Design

Backstamp: Gold printed semi-circular "Wade Made in England hand-painted" (1953-1961)

No.	Description	Colourways	Size	U.S. $	Can. $	U.K. £
1	Cream jug, small	White; copper trim; blue flowers, leaves	75	20.00	25.00	12.00

Blue Roses Design

Backstamp: Red printed "Wade England" (1953–c.1962)

No.	Description	Colourways	Size	U.S. $	Can. $	U.K. £
1	Cream jug, large	White; copper trim; blue flowers, leaves	90	20.00	30.00	12.00
2	Milk jug, medium		130	30.00	35.00	18.00
3	Milk jug, small		115	25.00	35.00	18.00

Clematis Design

This transfer printed design is of Clematis type flowers.

Photograph of design
not available
at press time

Backstamp: Red printed "Wade England" (1953–c.1965)

No.	Description	Colourways	Size	U.S. $	Can. $	U.K. £
1	Milk jug, medium	White; copper trim; white/yellow flowers; brown leaves	130	35.00	45.00	22.00

DANDY

Red Rose With Gypsophilia Design

Backstamp: Red printed "Wade England" (1953- c.1962)

No.	Description	Colourways	Size	U.S. $	Can. $	U.K. £
1	Cream jug, small	White; copper trim; red rose; small white flowers; green leaves	75	20.00	30.00	12.00

Yellow Daisy Design

Photograph of design
not available
at press time

Backstamp: Red printed "Wade England" (1953- c.1962)

No.	Description	Colourways	Size	U.S. $	Can. $	U.K. £
1	Milk jug, large	White; copper trim; yellow/black flowers; grey-green leaves	145	30.00	38.00	16.00

D
A
N
D
Y

VARIATION 4B WHITE BACKGROUND WITH TRANSFER PRINTS, WITHOUT COPPER LUSTRE HIGHLIGHTS

DANDY

Sunflowers Design

Photograph of design
not available
at press time

Backstamp: **A.** Green ink stamp "Wade Heath England" (round W 1937-1940)
B. Green ink stamp "Wade England A" (c.1945)
C. Red printed "Wade England" (1953- c.1962)

No.	Description	Colourways	Size	U.S. $	Can. $	U.K. £
1	Milk jug, large	White; yellow sunflowers; green leaves	145	32.00	42.00	20.00
2	Milk jug, medium		130	30.00	35.00	18.00
3	Milk jug, small		115	30.00	35.00	18.00

Thistle Chintz Design

Backstamp: Green ink stamp "Wade England A" (c.1945)

No.	Description	Colourways	Size	U.S. $	Can. $	U.K. £
1	Cream jug, small	Creamy yellow; mauve thistles; yellow gorse; green leaves	75	70.00	90.00	45.00
2	Sugar bowl, small		35	60.00	75.00	35.00

DONEGAL SHAPE, 1950-1970

There are two versions of Donegal cups and saucers. Version 1 has decorative rounded edges on the saucer which resemble shamrock leaves and the cup has a wavy rim. Version 2 (Shape No M336/337) is the traditional round shape. The plate (Shape No. M.344) has the shamrock design around the rim but in the centre is an embossed design of an Irish Colleen carrying peat to a cottage, a familiar design which has been used many times as a transfer print on Irish Wade products.

Backstamp: A. Embossed oval "Irish Porcelain (over a small shamrock) Made in Ireland" in Irish knot wreath with embossed "Design by James Borsey" added under wreath
   B. Embossed "Irish Porcelain (curved over shamrock) Made in Ireland by Wade Co. Armagh" in straight lines (c.1955-c.1985)
   C. Embossed circular Irish Porcelain (centre shamrock) "Made in Ireland" (with potters initial included) (c.1955-c.1985)
   D. Embossed "Made in Ireland Irish Porcelain (centre shamrock & crown) Wade eire tir A dheanta" (1971-1976)
   E. Embossed "Irish Porcelain (curved over shamrock and crown) Wade Ireland" (1977-1986) on cup, Impressed on saucer
   F. Embossed circular "Made in Ireland Porcelain (central small shamrock & crown) Wade eire tira dheanta"

No.	Description	Colourways	Size	U.S. $	Can. $	U.K. £
1	Coffee cup and saucer, Ver. 1	Blue-grey	63	40.00	50.00	25.00
2	Coffee cup and saucer, Ver. 2		72	30.00	40.00	18.00
3	Coffee pot		159	85.00	110.00	55.00
4	Cream jug		83	35.00	45.00	20.00
5	Milk jug, pint		153	70.00	90.00	45.00
6	Sugar bowl		62	35.00	45.00	20.00
7	Sugar bowl/lid		108	40.00	50.00	25.00
8	Tea plate, Colleen	Blue-grey-green	153	35.00	45.00	20.00
9	Tea plate, Colleen	Blue-grey-green	177	35.00	45.00	20.00

DONEGAL

FAIRY COTTAGE SHAPE, 1937

This set is similar in appearance to the Cottage Set found on page 33. The windows on Fairy Cottage are diamond lattice and on the Cottage Set they are square lattice.

F
A
I
R
Y

C
O
T
T
A
G
E

Backstamp: A. Ink stamp "Flaxman Ware Hand Made Pottery by Wadeheath England" with impressed "Fairy Cottage"
B. Black ink stamp "Flaxman Wade Heath England" with impressed "Fairy Cottage"

No.	Description	Colourways	Size	U.S. $	Can. $	U.K. £
1a	Honey/jam pot	Mottled green	101 x 76	65.00	85.00	40.00
1b	Honey/jam pot	Mottled grey blue	101 x 76	60.00	80.00	40.00
1c	Honey/jam pot	Orange	101 x 76	60.00	80.00	40.00
2a	Sugar bowl	Brown roof; red brown chimney; cream cottage; brown beams/door and window frames/ mushrooms; maroon/yellow/blue flowers	101 x 76	55.00	75.00	25.00
2b	Sugar bowl	Mottled green	101 x 76	35.00	45.00	18.00
2c	Sugar bowl	Orange	101 x 76	35.00	45.00	18.00

FESTIVAL SHAPE, 1951

The design on the Festival shape is a new colour variation of the Polka design. The new colourway was introduced in 1951, the year of the Festival of Britain, hence its new name.

Backstamp: Black printed "Wade Festival England"

No.	Description	Colourways	Size	U.S. $	Can. $	U.K. £
1	Cream jug	Creamy yellow; copper lustre highlighting; multi-coloured dancers	108	45.00	60.00	30.00
2	Milk jug, large		153	65.00	90.00	60.00
3	Milk jug, medium		140	65.00	90.00	50.00
4	Milk jug, small		127	50.00	65.00	35.00
5	Mug		123	60.00	80.00	40.00
6a	Nut dish	Creamy yellow; multi-coloured dancers	150	40.00	55.00	30.00
6b	Nut dish	Creamy yellow; copper lustre highlighting; multi-coloured dancers	150	35.00	45.00	24.00
7	Sugar bowl		57	40.00	50.00	25.00
8	Teapot, 6-cup		165	200.00	275.00	135.00

FLAIR SHAPE, 1953 - c.1965

BLUE DAISY DESIGN

Backstamp: Red printed "Wade England"

No.	Description	Colourways	Size	U.S. $	Can. $	U.K. £
1	Sugar bowl, small	White; copper trim; blue flowers/leaves	38	8.00	12.00	6.00

CARNIVAL DESIGN

The Carnival design was also used on decorative vases, jugs and dishes. *See The Charlton Standard Catalogue of Wade Volume Two: Decorative Wares.*

Backstamp: **A.** Red printed "Wade England" with or without the pattern name
B. Black printed "Wade England" with or without the pattern name

No.	Description	Colourways	Size	U.S. $	Can. $	U.K. £
1	Cup and saucer	Cup - white; yellow/orange flower; green leaves; yellow inner rim Saucer - yellow with white rim	63/146	12.00	16.00	8.00
2	Tea plate	White; yellow/orange flower; green leaves	165	8.00	12.00	6.00

COCKEREL DESIGN

Photograph of design
not available
at press time

Backstamp: Red printed "Wade England" with or without the pattern name

No.	Description	Colourways	Size	U.S. $	Can. $	U.K. £
1	Cup and saucer	White; yellow band; multi-coloured cockerel	63/146	22.00	30.00	15.00
2	Tea plate		165	15.00	20.00	10.00

FERN DESIGN

Backstamp: Black printed "Wade England" with or without the pattern name

No.	Description	Colourways	Size	U.S. $	Can. $	U.K. £
1	Cake plate	White; black/red fern leaves	240	15.00	20.00	10.00
2	Cup and saucer	Cup - white; black/red fern leaves; red interior Saucer - red with white rim	63/146	12.00	16.00	8.00
3	Tea plate	White; black/red fern leaves	165	6.00	8.00	4.00

GAIETY DESIGN

Photograph of design
not available
at press time

Backstamp: Red printed "Wade England" with or without the pattern name

No.	Description	Colourways	Size	U.S. $	Can. $	U.K. £
1	Cream jug, small	Turquoise outside, white inside	85	10.00	14.00	7.00
2	Cup and saucer	Cup - turquoise outside, white inside Saucer - white; pink/blue/grey flower spray	63/146	12.00	16.00	8.00
3	Sugar bowl, medium	Turquoise outside, white inside	50	6.00	8.00	4.00
4	Tea plate	White/turquoise; pink/blue/grey flower spray	165	6.00	8.00	4.00

F
L
A
I
R

GALAXY DESIGN

The Galaxy design was also used on decorative vases, jugs and dishes.

Backstamp: Black printed "Wade England" with or without the pattern name

No.	Description	Colourways	Size	U.S. $	Can. $	U.K. £
1	Cake plate	Black; yellow rim; black stars	240	25.00	35.00	18.00
2	Cream jug, small	White; black stars	85	10.00	14.00	7.00
3a	Cup and saucer	Cup - white outside/black stars; black inside Saucer - black with white rim	63/146	12.00	16.00	8.00
3b	Cup and saucer	Cup - white outside/black stars; black inside Saucer - black with yellow rim	63/146	12.00	16.00	8.00
4	Sugar bowl, large	White; black stars	65	8.00	12.00	6.00
5	Tea plate	Yellow/black; black stars	165	8.00	12.00	6.00
6	Teapot, 4-cup	White; black lid/stars	153	65.00	85.00	42.00
7	Teapot, 2-cup	White; black lid/stars	120	55.00	70.00	35.00

FLAIR

GAYDAY DESIGN

Backstamp: Black printed "Wade England" with or without the pattern name

No.	Description	Colourway	Size	U.S. $	Can. $	U.K. £
1	Cream jug, small	White; black/grey/red leaves; red stripe on handle	85	10.00	14.00	7.00
2	Cup and saucer	White; black/grey/red leaves	63/146	12.00	16.00	8.00
3	Sugar bowl, medium		50	8.00	12.00	6.00
4	Tea plate		165	8.00	12.00	6.00
5	Teapot, 4-cup	White; black/grey/red leaves; red stripe on handle	153	65.00	85.00	42.00
6	Teapot, 2-cup		120	55.00	70.00	35.00

GINGHAM DESIGN

Variation One

This gingham pattern has a broad crossed band with one thin wavy stripe.

For an illustration
of this design
see page 93

Backstamp: Red printed "Wade England" with or without the pattern name
Colourways: **A.** White; broad maroon bands; green wavy lines
B. White; broad green bands; maroon wavy lines

No.	Description	Size	U.S. $	Can. $	U.K. £
1	Cream jug, small	85	10.00	14.00	7.00
2	Cup and saucer	63/146	12.00	16.00	8.00
3	Tea plate	165	8.00	12.00	6.00
4	Teapot, 4-cup	153	65.00	85.00	42.00
5	Teapot, 2-cup	120	55.00	70.00	35.00

Variation Two

Backstamp: Black printed "Wade England" with or without the pattern name
Colourways: **A.** White; broad maroon bands, pink/black/yellow wavy lines
B. White; broad yellow bands, pink/black/yellow wavy lines

No.	Description	Size	U.S. $	Can. $	U.K. £
1	Cake plate	240	25.00	35.00	18.00
2	Cream jug, small	85	10.00	14.00	7.00
3	Cup and saucer	63/146	12.00	16.00	8.00
4	Tea plate	165	8.00	12.00	6.00

HONEYSUCKLE DESIGN

Backstamp: Black printed "Wade England" with or without the pattern name

No.	Description	Colourways	Size	U.S. $	Can. $	U.K. £
1	Cup and saucer	Cup - white; yellow/orange flower; black/green leaves; Saucer - green with white rim	63/146	12.00	18.00	8.00
2	Tea plate	White; green rim; yellow/orange flower; black/green leaves	165	8.00	12.00	6.00

PAGAN DESIGN

Backstamp: **A.** Black printed "Wade England" with or without the pattern name
B. Red printed "Wade England" with or without the pattern name

No.	Description	Colourways	Size	U.S. $	Can. $	U.K. £
1	Cream jug, small	White; red/white leaves	85	10.00	14.00	7.00
2	Cup and saucer	Cup - white; red/white leaves; Saucer - red/white; red/white leaves	63/146	12.00	16.00	8.00
3	Sugar bowl, medium	White; red/white leaves	50	8.00	12.00	6.00
4	Tea plate	Red/white; red/white leaves	165	8.00	12.00	6.00
5	Teapot, 2-cup	White; red/white leaves	120	55.00	70.00	35.00

PLANTAIN DESIGN, 1957

First advertised in May 1957 this design has a black plantain plant with yellow leaves.

Photograph of design
not available
at press time

Backstamp: Red printed "Wade England" with or without the pattern name

No.	Description	Colourways	Size	U.S. $	Can. $	U.K. £
1	Cup and saucer	Cup - white/red band; yellow/orange leaves; black/yellow seed heads Saucer - black; white rim	63/146	12.00	16.00	8.00
2	Tea plate	White/red band; yellow/orange leaves; black/yellow seed heads	165	8.00	12.00	6.00

POLKA DOT DESIGN, 1957

Advertised in May 1957, the Polka Dot design is black and white polka dots on black or red rimmed plates and saucers.

Backstamp: Red printed "Wade England" with or without the pattern name

No.	Description	Colourways	Size	U.S. $	Can. $	U.K. £
1a	Cup and saucer	Cup - white; black dots Saucer - black,white dots; white rim	63/146	12.00	14.00	8.00
1b	Cup and saucer	Cup — white; red dots Saucer - red; white rim; white dots	63/146	8.00	12.00	6.00
2a	Tea plate	White; black rim; white dots	165	8.00	12.00	6.00
2b	Tea plate	White; red rim; white dots	165	8.00	12.00	6.00

F
L
A
I
R

RED ROSE DESIGN

Only a sugar bowl has been reported with this red rose transfer printed design.

Backstamp: Red printed "Wade England"

No.	Description	Colourways	Size	U.S. $	Can. $	U.K. £
1	Sugar bowl, small	White; copper trim; small white flowers; red rose	38	8.00	12.00	6.00

ROSE HIP DESIGN

Backstamp: Red printed "Wade England" with or without the pattern name

No.	Description	Colourways	Size	U.S. $	Can. $	U.K. £
1	Cup and saucer	Cup - black interior; white; black/yellow leaves; red hip; Saucer - black; white rim	63/146	12.00	16.00	8.00
2	Tea plate	White; black/yellow leaves; red hips	165	8.00	12.00	6.00

F L A I R

SOUVENIRS DESIGN

A print of a red sail boat with the name of a popular British seaside resort or well-known British town is on these jugs. The Parasols design, seen on the Christchurch jug, was also used on the late 1950s Harmony Wares (see *The Charlton Standard Catalogue of Wade Vol. 2 Decorative Ware*).

F
L
A
I
R

Backstamp: Red printed "Wade England" with or without the pattern name

No.	Description	Colourways	Size	U.S. $	Can. $	U.K. £
1a	Broadstairs jug	White; red sails, blue sea; black lettering	85	15.00	20.00	10.00
1b	Christchurch jug	White; multi-coloured prints of parasols; black lettering	85	15.00	20.00	10.00
1c	Nova Scotia cup and saucer	White; multi-coloured print with lobster and trap	63/146	18.00	24.00	15.00
1d	Windsor Castle jug	White; gold rim; multi-coloured print	85	15.00	20.00	10.00

STARBURST DESIGN

Backstamp: Red printed "Wade England"

No.	Description	Colourways	Size	U.S. $	Can. $	U.K. £
1	Cake plate	White; black rays; red centre	240	25.00	35.00	18.00
2	Cup and saucer	Cup - white; black rays; red centre Saucer - red; white rim	63/146	8.00	10.00	5.00
3	Tea plate	White; black rays; red centre	165	6.00	10.00	5.00

STRIPED LEAF DESIGN

Backstamp: Red printed "Wade England" with or without the pattern name

No.	Description	Colourways	Size	U.S. $	Can. $	U.K. £
1	Cake plate	White/red; black/red striped leaves	240	25.00	35.00	18.00
2	Cream jug, large		105	10.00	14.00	7.00
3	Cup and saucer	Cup - white/red; black/red striped leaves Saucer - red; white rim	63/146	12.00	14.00	8.00
4	Sugar bowl, large	White; black/red striped leaves	65	8.00	12.00	6.00
5	Tea plate		165	8.00	12.00	6.00
6	Teapot, 4-cup		153	65.00	85.00	42.00

SUMMER ROSE DESIGN

Summer Rose was produced in both a pink and white and yellow and white colourway.

1. Pink Design

For an illustration
of this design
see page 70

Backstamp: A. Red printed "Wade England" with or without the pattern name
B. Black printed "Wade England" with or without the pattern name

No.	Description	Colourways	Size	U.S. $	Can. $	U.K. £
1	Cake plate	White; pink roses	240	25.00	35.00	18.00
2	Cream jug, large	Pale pink outside; white inside	105	10.00	14.00	7.00
3	Cup and saucer	Cup - pale pink/white; pink roses; green leaves; Saucer - white; pale pink roses; green leaves	63/146	12.00	14.00	8.00
4	Sugar bowl, large	Pink outside; white inside; pink rose	65	8.00	12.00	6.00
5	Sugar bowl, medium	Pink outside; white inside; pink rose	50	8.00	12.00	6.00
6	Tea plate	White; pink roses; green leaves	165	8.00	12.00	6.00

2. Yellow Design

For an illustration
of this design
see page 70

F L A I R

Backstamp: **A.** Red printed "Wade England" with or without the pattern name
B. Black printed "Wade England" with or without the pattern name

No.	Description	Colourways	Size	U.S. $	Can. $	U.K. £
1	Cake plate	White; yellow roses	240	25.00	35.00	18.00
2	Cream jug, large	Yellow outside; white inside	105	10.00	14.00	7.00
3	Cup and saucer	Cup - yellow/white; yellow roses; green leaves Saucer - white; yellow roses; green leaves	63/146	12.00	14.00	8.00
4	Sugar bowl, large	Yellow outside; white inside; yellow rose	65	8.00	12.00	6.00
5	Sugar bowl, medium	Yellow outside; white inside; yellow rose	50	8.00	12.00	6.00
6	Tea plate	White; yellow roses; green leaves	165	8.00	12.00	6.00

SUNFLOWER DESIGN

Backstamp: Black printed "Wade England" with or without the pattern name

No.	Description	Colourways	Size	U.S. $	Can. $	U.K. £
1	Cake plate	White; yellow/black flower; black/green leaves	240	25.00	35.00	18.00
2	Cup and saucer	Cup - white; yellow/black flower; black/green leaves; Saucer - dark green; white rim	63/146	12.00	16.00	8.00
3	Tea plate	White; yellow/black flower; black/green leaves	165	8.00	12.00	6.00
4	Teapot, 4-cup	White; yellow lid; yellow/black flower; black/green leaves	153	65.00	85.00	42.00

TWO TONE DESIGN

Two Tone was produced in both a black and green and chocolate and peach colourway.

1. Black and Green Design

Photograph of design
not available
at press time

Backstamp: Black printed "Wade England" with or without the pattern name

No.	Description	Colourways	Size	U.S. $	Can. $	U.K. £
1	Cup and saucer	Cup - green; Saucer - black	63/146	8.00	10.00	5.00
2	Tea plate	Green	165	12.00	16.00	8.00

2. Chocolate and Peach Design

Photograph of design
not available
at press time

Backstamp: Black printed "Wade England" with or without the pattern name

No.	Description	Colourways	Size	U.S. $	Can. $	U.K. £
1	Cup and saucer	Cup - peach; Saucer - chocolate	63/146	8.00	10.00	5.00
2	Tea plate	Peach	165	12.00	16.00	8.00

UMBRELLA PLANT DESIGN

Backstamp: Red printed "Wade England"

No.	Description	Colourways	Size	U.S. $	Can. $	U.K. £
1	Cake plate	White; grey striped border; black/red/grey leaves; red stems	240	25.00	35.00	18.00
2	Tea plate	White; black/red/grey leaves; red stems	165	8.00	12.00	6.00
3	Teapot, 2-cup	White; grey striped finial/handle; black/red/grey leaves; red stems	120	55.00	70.00	35.00

F L A I R

VIOLET DESIGN

Violet flowers on a primrose background.

Photograph of design
not available
at press time

Backstamp: Black printed "Wade England" with or without the pattern name

No.	Description	Colourways	Size	U.S. $	Can. $	U.K. £
1	Cup and saucer	Cup - primrose; violet flowers; green leaves Saucer - white; violet flowers; green leaves	63/146	12.00	16.00	8.00
2	Cream jug, small	Primrose outside; white inside	85	10.00	14.00	7.00
3	Sugar bowl, large	Primrose outside; white inside	65	8.00	12.00	6.00
4	Tea plate	White; violet flowers; green leaves	165	8.00	12.00	6.00

WILD ROSE DESIGN

The jug and teapot are white on the inside and pink on the outside with pink flowers. The cups and sugar bowl are pink outside with pink flowers inside.

Photograph of design
not available
at press time

Backstamp: Black printed "Wade England" with or without the pattern name

No.	Description	Colourways	Size	U.S. $	Can. $	U.K. £
1	Cake plate	White; pink rose spray; green leaves	240	25.00	35.00	18.00
2	Cream jug, small	Outside — pink; pink rose spray; Inside — white	85	10.00	14.00	7.00
3	Cup and saucer	Cup - pink outside; white inside with pink rose spray; green leaves; Saucer - white; pink rose spray; green leaves	63/146	12.00	16.00	8.00
4	Sugar bowl, large	Pink outside; white inside with pink rose spray; green leaves	65	8.00	12.00	6.00
5	Tea plate	White; pink rose spray; green leaves	165	8.00	12.00	6.00
6	Teapot, 4-cup	Outside — pink; pink rose spray; Inside — white	153	65.00	85.00	42.00

WOODMIST DESIGN

Woodmist was produced in three colours with dominant black, green or red fern like leaves. Each colour has a different small flower design. The saucers are black, green or red with a white rim.

1. Black Fern Design

Photograph of colourway
not available
at press time

Backstamp: A. Red printed "Wade England" with or without the pattern name
B. Black printed "Wade England" with or without the pattern name

No.	Description	Colourways	Size	U.S. $	Can. $	U.K. £
1	Cake plate	White; black/grey leaves; red/yellow pointed flower	240	25.00	35.00	18.00
2	Cup and saucer	Cup - white; black/grey leaves; red/yellow pointed flower; Saucer - black; white rim	63/146	12.00	16.00	8.00
3	Tea plate	White; black/grey leaves; red/yellow pointed flower	165	8.00	12.00	6.00

FLAIR

2. Green Fern Design

Backstamp: A. Red printed "Wade England" with or without the pattern name
B. Black printed "Wade England" with or without the pattern name

No.	Description	Colourways	Size	U.S. $	Can. $	U.K. £
1	Cake plate	White; green/grey leaves; yellow/orange round flower	240	25.00	35.00	18.00
2	Cup and saucer	Cup - white; green/grey leaves; yellow/orange round flower; Saucer - green; white rim	63/146	12.00	16.00	8.00
3	Tea plate	White; green/grey leaves; yellow/orange round flower	165	8.00	12.00	6.00

3. Red Fern Design

Backstamp: A. Red printed "Wade England" with or without the pattern name
B. Black printed "Wade England" with or without the pattern name

No.	Description	Colourways	Size	U.S. $	Can. $	U.K. £
1	Cake plate	White; red/grey leaves; blue star flower	240	25.00	35.00	18.00
2	Cream jug, small		85	10.00	14.00	7.00
3	Cup and saucer	Cup - white; red/grey leaves; blue star flower; Saucer - red; white rim	63/146	12.00	16.00	8.00
4	Sugar bowl, large	White; red/grey leaves; blue star flower	65	8.00	12.00	6.00
5	Sugar bowl, medium		50	8.00	12.00	6.00
6	Tea plate		165	8.00	12.00	6.00
7	Teapot, 2-cup		120	65.00	85.00	45.00

F
L
A
I
R

FAMILY FOUR (THE)

A small picnic set called the Family Four was available in any of the colours listed and consisted of 4 cups, saucers and tea plates.

Backstamp: Red printed "Wade England"

No.	Description	Colourways	Size	U.S. $	Can. $	U.K. £
1a	Cup and saucer	Cup - grey/white; pale pink roses; green leaves Saucer - white; pink roses; green leaves	63/146	12.00	16.00	8.00
1b	Cup and saucer	Cup - light green/white; pink roses; green leaves Saucer - white; pink roses; green leaves	63/146	12.00	16.00	8.00
1c	Cup and saucer	Cup - pale blue/white; pink roses; green leaves Saucer - white; pink roses; green leaves	63/146	8.00	10.00	5.00
1d	Cup and saucer	Cup - pale pink/white; pink roses; green leaves Saucer - white; pink roses; green leaves	63/146	8.00	10.00	5.00
2	Tea plate	White; pink roses; green leaves	165	8.00	12.00	6.00

FLAIR

GARDEN TRELLIS SHAPE, 1934-c.1945

A similar set was produced using the same colour combinations with a stone garden wall as the base and a squirrel finial. (See Garden Wall set on page 73).

Biscuit Barrel

Butter Dish

Cheese Dish

Teapot

GARDEN TRELLIS

Backstamp: **A.** Ink stamp "Wadeheath Ware England" (1934-1937)
B. Ink stamp "Wade Heath England" (round W 1937-1940)
C. Ink stamp "Wade Heath England A" (round W 1939-1945)

Cruet

No.	Description	Colourways	Size	U.S. $	Can. $	U.K. £
1	Biscuit barrel, large	Cream; dark brown trellis; light brown rocks; dark grey bird bath; maroon/yellow flowers; green leaves; brown bird finial	159	135.00	180.00	90.00
2	Biscuit barrel, small	Cream; dark brown trellis; light brown rocks; light grey bird bath; maroon/yellow flowers; green leaves; brown bird finial	146	135.00	180.00	90.00
3a	Butter dish, round	Cream; brown trellis; light brown rocks; grey bird bath; maroon/yellow flowers; green leaves; brown bird finial	108	80.00	110.00	55.00
3b	Butter dish, round	Cream; green/brown trellis; dark/light brown rocks; dark grey bird bath; maroon/yellow flowers; green leaves; brown bird finial	108	80.00	110.00	55.00
4a	Cheese dish, wedge	Cream; dark brown trellis; light brown rocks; grey bird bath; maroon/yellow flowers; green leaves; brown bird finial	114	90.00	120.00	60.00
4b	Cheese dish, wedge	Cream; light brown trellis; grey rocks; grey bird bath; yellow/purple flowers; green leaves; yellow bird finial	114	90.00	120.00	60.00
5	Cream jug	Cream; dark brown trellis; light brown rocks maroon/yellow flowers; green leaves; brown birds	114	70.00	90.00	45.00
6	Cruet	Creamy brown; maroon/purple flowers; brown bird finial on mustard pot	65	55.00	70.00	40.00
7	Honey pot	Cream; light/dark brown crazy paving; maroon/purple flowers; green leaves; brown bird finial	95	80.00	105.00	55.00
8	Hot water jug	Cream; green/brown trellis; light grey rocks; grey bird bath; maroon/yellow flowers; green leaves; brown bird finial	177	135.00	180.00	90.00
9	Hot water jug	Cream; dark brown trellis; light brown rocks; grey bird bath; maroon/yellow flowers; green leaves; brown bird finial	184	135.00	180.00	90.00
10	Sugar bowl	Cream; dark brown trellis; light brown rocks; maroon/yellow flowers; green leaves;	88	65.00	70.00	35.00
11	Teapot, 4-cup	Cream; dark brown trellis; light brown rocks; grey bird bath; maroon/yellow flowers; green leaves; brown bird finial	146	135.00	180.00	90.00

GARDEN WALL SHAPE, 1935-1937

A similar set was produced in the same colours with a bird as the lid finial and a garden rockery base. (See Garden Trellis set on page 71).

Teapot and Hot Water Jug

Biscuit Barrel

Backstamp: Ink stamp "Wade Heath England" (1935-1937)

No.	Description	Colourways	Size	U.S. $	Can. $	U.K. £
1	Biscuit barrel	Cream; brown tree; light brown wall/archway; maroon/yellow flowers; green leaves; brown squirrel finial	153	135.00	180.00	90.00
2	Butter dish	Cream; brown tree; light brown wall; maroon/yellow flowers; green leaves; brown squirrel finial	108	80.00	110.00	55.00
3	Cheese dish, wedge	Cream;w brown tree; light brown wall; maroon/yellow flowers; green leaves; brown squirrel finial	114	90.00	120.00	60.00
4	Cream jug	Cream; brown tree; light brown wall; maroon/yellow flowers; green leaves	114	70.00	90.00	45.00
5	Hot water jug	Cream; brown tree; light brown wall; maroon/yellow flowers; green leaves; brown squirrel finial	170	135.00	180.00	90.00
6	Sugar bowl	Cream; brown tree; light brown wall; maroon/yellow flowers; green leaves	88	65.00	70.00	35.00
7	Teapot, 4-cup	Cream; brown tree; light brown wall; maroon/yellow flowers; green leaves; brown squirrel finial	146	135.00	180.00	90.00

GRAPE SHAPE, c.1948-c.1962

The Grape Shape is found in a set of Tea and Supper wares produced with an embossed design of grapes and vine leaves. There are seven different colourways. Only the cream coloured sugar bowl has a chrome lid, all other lids are ceramic.

CREAM DESIGN

Photograph of colourway
not available at press time

Backstamp: Green ink stamp "Wade England"

No.	Description	Colourways	Size	U.S. $	Can. $	U.K. £
1	Sugar bowl, chrome lid	White/cream; dark red grapes; green/blue leaves	88	35.00	45.00	20.00

DARK GREEN/WHITE DESIGN

Photograph of
colourway not available
at press time

Backstamp: Gold printed semi-circular "Wade Made in England Hand Painted"

No.	Description	Colourways	Size	U.S. $	Can. $	U.K. £
1	Milk jug	Dark green; white grapes/leaves	145	35.00	45.00	25.00
2	Sauce boat/stand	Sauce boat - dark green; white grapes/leaves; Stand - dark green	76 x 153	35.00	45.00	25.00

GREENTONE DESIGN

Backstamp: **A.** Green ink stamp "Wade England"
B. Gold printed semi-circular "Wade Made in England Hand Painted"
C. Gold printed circular "Royal Victoria Pottery Wade England" (1960-1970)

No.	Description	Colourways	Size	U.S. $	Can. $	U.K. £
1	Cake plate	Olive green; off white grapes/leaves; gold rim	280	50.00	65.00	35.00
2	Cup and saucer		70/140	60.00	75.00	30.00
3	Plate		225	45.00	60.00	28.00
4	Salt and pepper	Olive green; gold grapes/leaves	57	38.00	50.00	25.00
5	Sauce boat/stand	Olive green; off white grapes/leaves	76 x 153	35.00	45.00	25.00
6	Sugar bowl, lid	Olive green; off white grapes/leaves	88	45.00	60.00	30.00
7	Tea plate	Olive green; off white grapes/leaves; gold rim	170	22.00	30.00	15.00

REGAL GREEN DESIGN

G
R
A
P
E

Backstamp: A. Gold printed semi-circular "Wade Made in England Hand Painted"
B. Gold printed circular "Royal Victoria Pottery Wade England" (1960-1970)

No.	Description	Colourways	Size	U.S. $	Can. $	U.K. £
1	Cream jug	Dark green; gold grapes/leaves; gold rim	88	45.00	60.00	30.00
2	Cruet	Dark green; gold grapes/leaves; gold rim Tray - dark green; gold band	57 x 108	60.00	80.00	40.00
3	Cup and saucer	Dark green; gold grapes/leaves; gold rim	70/140	60.00	75.00	30.00
4	Salt and pepper		57	38.00	50.00	25.00
5	Sugar bowl		88	35.00	45.00	22.00

REGAL WHITE DESIGN

Backstamp: A. Green ink stamp "Wade England"
B. Gold printed semi-circular "Wade Made in England Hand Painted"

No.	Description	Colourways	Size	U.S. $	Can. $	U.K. £
1	Cream jug	White; gold grapes/leaves	88	45.00	60.00	30.00
2	Milk jug	White; gold foot/grapes/leaves	145	35.00	45.00	25.00
3	Sauce boat/stand	Sauce boat - white; gold grapes/leaves; Stand - white; gold rim	76 x 153	35.00	45.00	25.00
4	Sugar bowl, lid	White; gold grapes/leaves	88	45.00	60.00	30.00
5	Teapot, 6-cup		153	80.00	105.00	50.00

RUBYTONE DESIGN

Sugar Bowl with Lid

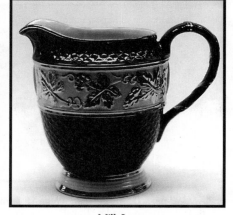

Milk Jug

Backstamp: Gold printed semi-circular "Wade Made in England Hand Painted, Rubytone"

No.	Description	Colourways	Size	U.S. $	Can. $	U.K. £
1	Butter dish, lid	Ruby red; white band; gold grapes/leaves	unknown	35.00	40.00	20.00
2	Cheese dish, lid	Ruby red; white band; gold grapes/leaves	101 x 221	55.00	70.00	35.00
3	Cream jug		88	45.00	60.00	30.00
4	Cruet	Ruby red; white band; gold grapes/leaves tray - ruby red; gold band	57 x 108	60.00	80.00	40.00
5	Cup and saucer	Ruby red; white band; gold grapes/leaves	70/140	60.00	75.00	30.00
6	Fruit bowl, small		127	65.00	90.00	45.00
7	Fruit bowl, large		177	65.00	90.00	45.00
8	Milk jug		145	35.00	45.00	25.00
9	Plate		225	45.00	60.00	28.00
10	Preserve bowl, handles		88 x 159	50.00	65.00	32.00
11	Salad bowl	Ruby red; white band/foot; gold grapes/leaves	88 x 280	80.00	105.00	50.00
12	Salad servers	Ruby red; gold grapes/leaves	216	40.00	50.00	25.00
13	Salt and pepper	Ruby red; white band; gold grapes/leaves	57	38.00	50.00	25.00
14	Sauce boat/stand		76 x 153	35.00	45.00	25.00
15	Sugar bowl, lid	Ruby red; white band; gold grapes/leaves	88	45.00	60.00	30.00
16	Tea plate		170	22.00	30.00	15.00
17	Teapot, 6-cup		153	80.00	105.00	50.00
18	Teapot, 4-cup		140	70.00	90.00	45.00
19	Teapot, 2-cup		101	50.00	65.00	35.00

GRAPE

WHITETONE DESIGN

Backstamp: Gold printed semi-circular "Wade Made in England Hand Painted"

No.	Description	Colourways	Size	U.S. $	Can. $	U.K. £
1	Cup and saucer	White; light green grapes; dark green leaves	70/140	60.00	75.00	30.00
2	Teapot, 6-cup		153	80.00	105.00	50.00

IONA SHAPE, c.1927-1933

FLORAL BAND DESIGN

Photograph of design
not available
at press time

Backstamp: Red ink stamp "Wade England" with lion

No.	Description	Colourways	Size	U.S. $	Can. $	U.K. £
1	Hot water jug	White; multi-coloured floral band	185	85.00	100.00	50.00
2	Milk jug		146	45.00	60.00	30.00
3	Stand for teapot		146	40.00	50.00	25.00
4	Teapot, 4-cup		146	65.00	85.00	45.00

GOLD FLOWERS DESIGN

Backstamp: Red ink stamp "Wade England" with lion

No.	Description	Colourways	Size	U.S. $	Can. $	U.K. £
1	Hot water jug	Black; gold bands/flowers	185	90.00	110.00	55.00
2	Milk jug		146	60.00	90.00	45.00
3	Stand for teapot		146	55.00	70.00	35.00
4	Teapot, 4-cup		146	100.00	120.00	65.00

GOLD JIGSAW DESIGN

Backstamp: Red ink stamp "Wade England" with lion

No.	Description	Colourways	Size	U.S. $	Can. $	U.K. £
1	Hot water jug	Royal blue; gold design	185	90.00	110.00	55.00
2	Milk jug		146	60.00	90.00	45.00
3	Stand for teapot		146	40.00	50.00	25.00
4	Teapot, 4-cup		146	90.00	110.00	55.00

PAISLEY DESIGN

Backstamp: Red ink stamp "Wade England" with lion

No.	Description	Colourways	Size	U.S. $	Can. $	U.K. £
1	Hot water jug	Multi-coloured paisley print	185	190.00	250.00	125.00
2	Milk jug		146	150.00	200.00	100.00
3	Stand for teapot		146	75.00	100.00	50.00
4	Teapot, 4-cup		146	190.00	250.00	125.00

LATTICE SHAPE, c.1948-c.1958

COPPER LUSTRE DESIGN

Cruet

Jam Pot

Backstamp: Green ink stamp "Wade England" (crossed W c.1948-1953)

No.	Description	Colourways	Size	U.S. $	Can. $	U.K. £
1	Cream jug	Copper lustre; white flowers/leaves	70	35.00	45.00	25.00
2	Cruet		unknown	30.00	40.00	20.00
3	Jam pot		112	45.00	60.00	30.00
4	Oval dish, extra large		266	45.00	60.00	30.00
5	Oval dish, large		205	45.00	60.00	30.00
6	Oval dish, medium		153	30.00	40.00	20.00

GREEN DESIGN

Backstamp: A. Green ink stamp "Wade England" (crossed W c.1948-1953)
B. Gold printed "Wade Made In England Hand Painted" (1953-c.1958)

No.	Description	Colourways	Size	U.S. $	Can. $	U.K. £
1	Bowl, curved handles	Pale green; red flowers/dots; black leaves	133	25.00	35.00	17.00
2	Bowl, curved handles		159	25.00	35.00	17.00
3	Biscuit barrel		165	45.00	60.00	30.00
4	Butter dish		76 x 114	25.00	35.00	17.00
5	Cheese dish		88 x 158	35.00	45.00	25.00
6	Cream jug		70	25.00	35.00	17.00
7	Cruet		unknown	25.00	35.00	17.00
8	Jam pot		112	35.00	45.00	25.00
9	Milk jug		127	35.00	45.00	25.00
10	Oval dish, large		205	35.00	45.00	25.00
11	Oval dish, medium		153	30.00	40.00	20.00
12	Oval dish, small		127	25.00	35.00	17.00
13	Salad bowl		210	40.00	55.00	25.00
14	Salad servers		210	25.00	35.00	18.00
15	Sauce boat and stand		63 x 155	25.00	35.00	17.00
16	Sugar bowl		55	8.00	12.00	6.00
17	Teapot, 6-cup		165	60.00	80.00	40.00
18	Triple tray		unknown	25.00	35.00	17.00

LATTICE

SILVER LUSTRE DESIGN

Cream Jug

Salad Bowl

Backstamp: Gold printed "Wade Made In England Hand Painted" (1953-c.1958)

No.	Description	Colourways	Size	U.S. $	Can. $	U.K. £
1	Cream jug	Silver; white flowers/leaves	70	40.00	55.00	28.00
2	Milk jug		127	45.00	60.00	30.00
3	Salad bowl		210	65.00	85.00	40.00

WHITE PEARL DESIGN

Backstamp: **A.** Green ink stamp "Wade England" (crossed W c.1948-1953)
B. Gold printed "Wade Made In England Hand Painted" (1953- c.1958)

No.	Description	Colourways	Size	U.S. $	Can. $	U.K. £
1	Bowl, curved handles	White pearl; yellow/red flowers; green leaves	159	25.00	35.00	17.00
2	Cheese dish	White pearl; red finial; yellow/red flowers; green leaves	88 x 158	35.00	45.00	25.00
3	Teapot, 6-cup		165	60.00	80.00	40.00

YELLOW DESIGN

Photograph of design
not available
at press time

Backstamp: Gold printed "Wade Made In England Hand Painted" (1953-c.1958)

No.	Description	Colourways	Size	U.S. $	Can. $	U.K. £
1	Butter dish	Yellow; yellow/red flowers; green leaves	76 x 114	25.00	35.00	17.00
2	Cream jug		70	25.00	35.00	17.00

LATTICE

LETTUCE LEAF SHAPE, 1938-c.1940

The irregular shaped heavily embossed dish is an open lettuce leaf with embossed tomatoes and a fish on the edge. The cruet has a lettuce leaf shaped tray with an embossed fish on one end, the salt and pepper pots are long-leafed cos lettuces and the mustard pot is a tomato, the cos lettuce honey pot has a tomato shaped lid with a recess for a spoon.

Honey Pot, Cruet

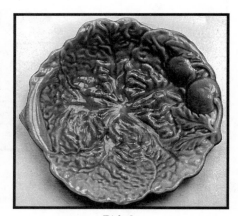

Dish, 2a

Backstamp: Green ink stamp "Wade Heath England" (round W 1937-1940)

No.	Description	Colourways	Size	U.S. $	Can. $	U.K. £
1	Cruet	Green	55 x 127	40.00	55.00	28.00
2a	Dish	Green	216	40.00	55.00	28.00
2b	Dish	Green; dark red tomatoes	216	40.00	55.00	28.00
3	Honey/jam pot	Green	109	45.00	60.00	30.00
4	Salt and pepper	Green	55	25.00	35.00	18.00
5	Sauce boat/stand	Green; dark red tomatoes	127	40.00	45.00	20.00

MEDALLION SHAPE, c.1960

Backstamp: A. Embossed oval "Irish Porcelain (over a small shamrock) Made in Ireland" in
Irish knot wreath with embossed "Design by James Borsey" added under wreath
B. Embossed oval "Irish Porcelain (over a small shamrock) Made in Ireland" in Irish
knot wreath (no signature)

No.	Description	Colourways	Size	U.S. $	Can. $	U.K. £
1	Cream jug	Blue-grey	90	30.00	40.00	20.00
2	Sugar bowl		55	30.00	40.00	20.00
3	Teapot, 8-cup		180	95.00	125.00	60.00
4	Teapot, 6-cup		155	80.00	100.00	50.00

MODE SHAPE, c.1948 - c.1965

First introduced in the late 1940s in chintz, hand-painted and one-colour designs, the Mode (Modern style) combination tea/supper sets can be found in a large number of different designs.

A hand-painted design named Capri first used in the late 1940s was still being advertised in the *Pottery Gazette and Glass Trade Review* in July of 1953 and also listed as "Our Current Line" in the Spring 1954 edition of the Wade Pottery magazine, *The Jolly Potter*.

BALL FLOWER DESIGN, c.1950-c.1960

Backstamp: Black printed circular "Royal Victoria Pottery Wade England" (c.1952-1960)

No.	Description	Colourways	Size	U.S. $	Can. $	U.K. £
1	Cup and saucer	White; pink ball flower; blue/yellow/ green leaves	60/143	12.00	16.00	8.00
2	Dinner plate		240	18.00	25.00	12.00
3	Lunch plate		205	15.00	20.00	8.00
4	Tea plate		153	9.00	12.00	6.00
5	TV set		60/242	40.00	65.00	30.00

BANDED DESIGN

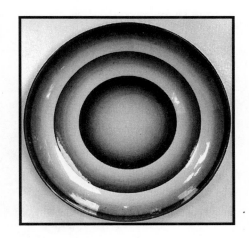

Backstamp: **A.** Black ink stamp "Wade England"
B. Black printed circular "Royal Victoria Pottery Wade England" (c.1952-1960)

No.	Description	Colourways	Size	U.S. $	Can. $	U.K. £
1	Cream jug	Green/purple/maroon bands	63	10.00	12.00	6.00
2	Cup and saucer		60/143	12.00	16.00	8.00
3	Sugar bowl		63	10.00	12.00	6.00
4	Tea plate		153	9.00	12.00	6.00

CAPRI DESIGN, c.1948-c.1955

A set of four cups, saucers, oatmeal bowls, tea plates and lunch plates was advertised in the mid 1950s by a Toronto China store for $6.40 (approx. £3.20p) a set.

Backstamp: **A.** Black ink stamp "Wade England" (crossed W c.1948-1953)
B. Black printed circular "Royal Victoria Pottery Wade England" (1950-1960)

No.	Description	Colourways	Size	U.S. $	Can. $	U.K. £
1	Cup and saucer	White; green rim; maroon/yellow tulips; blue flowers; brown/green leaves	65/143	20.00	25.00	12.00
2	Dinner plate		240	25.00	35.00	15.00
3	Lunch plate		205	20.00	25.00	12.00
4	Oatmeal bowl		190	15.00	20.00	10.00
5	Tea plate		153	15.00	20.00	10.00

CARNIVAL DESIGN

The carnival design was also used on decorative vases, jugs and dishes (see *The Charlton Standard Catalogue of Wade, Volume Two Decorative Wares*).

For an illustration
of this design
see page 56

Backstamp: Black printed circular "Royal Victoria Pottery Wade England" (c.1952-1960)

No.	Description	Colourways	Size	U.S. $	Can. $	U.K. £
1	Cup and saucer	Cup — white; yellow/orange flower; green leaves; Saucer — yellow; white rim	60/143	10.00	12.00	6.00
2	TV set	White; yellow/orange flower; green leaves	60/242	35.00	45.00	24.00

DAHLIA DESIGN

Backstamp: A. Black ink stamp "Wade England" (crossed W c.1948-1953)
B. Black printed circular "Royal Victoria Pottery Wade England" (c.1952-1960)

No.	Description	Colourways	Size	U.S. $	Can. $	U.K. £
1	Dinner plate	White; large yellow flower; brown streaks; green leaves	240	25.00	35.00	15.00

DARWIN CHINTZ DESIGN

This design was available in three colourways.

Variation One — Blue

Backstamp: Blue ink stamp "Wade England Darwin"

No.	Description	Colourways	Size	U.S. $	Can. $	U.K. £
1	Cup and saucer	Speckled blue; white/blue flowers/leaves	60/143	55.00	75.00	35.00
2	Sandwich plate, oval		175	40.00	50.00	25.00
3	Sugar bowl		63	45.00	60.00	30.00
4	Tea plate		153	40.00	52.00	28.00

Variation Two — Brown

For an illustration
of this design
see previous page

Backstamp: **A.** Brown ink stamp "Wade England Darwin" (c.1948)
B. Black ink stamp "Wade England" (crossed W c.1948-1953)

No.	Description	Colourways	Size	U.S. $	Can. $	U.K. £
1	Cup and saucer	Speckled brown; white/brown flowers/leaves	60/143	55.00	75.00	35.00
2	Sandwich plate, oval		175	40.00	50.00	25.00
3	Sugar bowl		63	45.00	60.00	30.00
4	Tea plate		153	40.00	52.00	28.00

Variation Three — Green

For an illustration
of this design
see previous page

Backstamp: **A.** Brown ink stamp "Wade England Darwin" (c.1948)
B. Black ink stamp "Wade England" (crossed W c.1948-1953)

No.	Description	Colourways	Size	U.S. $	Can. $	U.K. £
1	Cup and saucer	Speckled green; white/brown flowers/leaves	60/143	55.00	75.00	35.00
2	Sandwich plate, oval		175	40.00	50.00	25.00
3	Sugar bowl		63	45.00	60.00	30.00
4	Tea plate		153	40.00	52.00	28.00

DIAMONDS DESIGN

Backstamp: Printed "Wade England Diamond 1640"

No.	Description	Colourways	Size	U.S. $	Can. $	U.K. £
1	Cup and saucer	White; red chequered diamonds; black stripes	60/143	12.00	16.00	8.00
2	Salt and pepper		90	18.00	25.00	12.00
3	Tea plate		153	10.00	13.00	6.00

MODE

FERN DESIGN

The Flair teapot was used in this Mode set.

Backstamp: Unknown

No.	Description	Colourways	Size	U.S. $	Can. $	U.K. £
1	Cup and saucer	White; black and red fern leaves	60/143	12.00	16.00	8.00
2	Dinner plate		240	20.00	30.00	15.00
3	Tea plate		153	10.00	13.00	16.00
4	Teapot, 4-cup		153	65.00	85.00	45.00

MODE

GINGHAM DESIGN

Variation One

Backstamp: Black printed circular "Royal Victoria Pottery Wade England" (c.1952-1960)
Colourways: A. White; green bands; maroon line
B. White; maroon bands; green line

No.	Description	Size	U.S. $	Can. $	U.K. £
1	Cream jug	63	10.00	12.00	6.00
2	Cruet	75	30.00	40.00	20.00
3	Cup and saucer	60/143	12.00	16.00	8.00
4	Dessert bowl	165	12.00	15.00	6.00
5	Dinner plate	240	18.00	25.00	12.00
6	Platter, large	343	25.00	35.00	18.00
7	Platter, small	266	20.00	27.00	14.00
8	Sugar bowl	63	10.00	12.00	6.00
9	Tea plate	153	10.00	13.00	6.00
10	Water jug	248	40.00	50.00	25.00

Variation Two

Backstamp: Black printed circular "Royal Victoria Pottery Wade England" (c.1952-1960)
Colourways: A. White; dark green bands; black/yellow/pink lines
B. White; maroon bands; black/yellow/maroon lines

No.	Description	Size	U.S. $	Can. $	U.K. £
1	Cake plate	160	10.00	13.00	6.00
2	TV set	60/242	35.00	45.00	24.00

HARVEST DESIGN, c.1962

Backstamp: Gold circular printed "Royal Victoria Pottery Wade England" (1960-1970)

No.	Description	Colourways	Size	U.S. $	Can. $	U.K. £
1	Cup and saucer	White; yellow/green grains; yellow/brown/ green leaves	60/143	10.00	12.00	6.00
2	Dinner plate		240	12.00	18.00	9.00
3	Tea plate		153	10.00	13.00	6.00

MODE

RITA DESIGN

The Rita design is of vine leaves and berries. A set of four cups, saucers, oatmeal bowls, tea plates and lunch plates was advertised in the mid 1950s by a Toronto China store for $5.84 (approx. £3) a set.

Photograph of design
not available
at press time

Backstamp: Black printed circular "Royal Victoria Pottery Wade England" (c.1952-1960)

No.	Description	Colourways	Size	U.S. $	Can. $	U.K. £
1	Cup and saucer	White; green vine leaves; red berries	60 /143	15.00	20.00	10.00
2	Dinner plate		240	18.00	25.00	12.00
3	Oatmeal bowl		190	12.00	15.00	6.00
4	Sugar bowl with lid		95	25.00	35.00	20.00
5	Tea plate		153	9.00	12.00	6.00

SHOOTING STAR DESIGN

 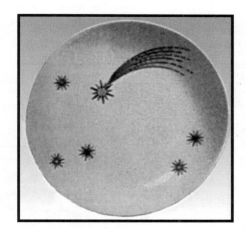

Backstamp: Unknown

No.	Description	Colourways	Size	U.S. $	Can. $	U.K. £
1	Cake plate	White; black stars	160	9.00	12.00	6.00
2	Cream jug	White; red interior; black stars	63	8.00	10.00	5.00
3	Cup and saucer	Cup - black interior; white; black stars Saucer - black with white rim	60/143	10.00	12.00	6.00
4	Sugar bowl	White; black/multi-coloured stars	63	8.00	10.00	5.00
5	Tea plate	White; black/multi-coloured stars	153	10.00	13.00	6.00

SOLID DESIGN

MODE

Backstamp: Black ink stamp "Wade England" (crossed W c.1948-1953)
Colourways: **A.** Grey
              B. Maroon

No.	Description	Size	U.S. $	Can. $	U.K. £
1	Cup and saucer	60/143	10.00	12.00	6.00
2	Tea plate	153	10.00	13.00	6.00

SORRENTO DESIGN

Backstamp: Black printed circular "Royal Victoria Pottery Wade England Sorrento" (c.1952-1960)

No.	Description	Colourways	Size	U.S. $	Can. $	U.K. £
1	Platter, large	White; green rim; maroon/purple flowers; blue flower buds; green/brown leaves	343	35.00	45.00	22.00

STARBURST DESIGN

Backstamp: Black printed "Wade England"

No.	Description	Colourways	Size	U.S. $	Can. $	U.K. £
1	Cake plate	White; red centred stars	160	9.00	12.00	6.00
2	Cream jug	Red interior; white; red centred stars	63	8.00	10.00	5.00
3	Cup and saucer	Cup - red interior; white; red centred stars	65/143	10.00	12.00	6.00
		Saucer - white; red centred stars				
4	Sugar bowl	Red interior; white; red centred stars	63	8.00	10.00	5.00
5	Tea plate	White; red centred stars	153	10.00	13.00	6.00

STRIPED LEAF DESIGN

This design was also used on Flair tablewares (see page 65).

Backstamp: **A.** Black ink stamp "Wade England" (crossed W c.1948-1953)
B. Gold printed circular "Royal Victoria Pottery Wade England" (1960-1970)

No.	Description	Colourways	Size	U.S. $	Can. $	U.K. £
1	Cup and saucer	Cup - red interior; white; black/red striped leaves;	60/143	12.00	16.00	8.00
		Saucer - white/red				
2	Dish with handle	White; black/red striped leaves	unknown	15.00	20.00	10.00

MOURNE SHAPE / DESIGN, 1971-1976

These items in Irish Mourne colours have an impressed rose design except for the preserve jar which is decorated with blackberries. Other items produced in the Mourne range were vases, dishes, tankards and a candy box (see *The Charlton Standard Catalogue of Wade, Volumes 1 and 2*).

Item	Irish Wade Shape No.
Butter Dish	C.355
Milk Jug	C.356
Pepper	C.359
Salt	C.358
Sugar Bowl	C.357

Butter Dish

Preserve Pot

Backstamp: Embossed circular "Made in Ireland Porcelain" (central small shamrock and crown) "Wade eire tira dheanta" (1971-1976)

No.	Description	Colourways	Size	U.S. $	Can. $	U.K. £
1	Butter dish with lid	Brown-green; orange rose	57 x 95	45.00	60.00	30.00
2	Milk jug	Green-brown; orange rose	108	65.00	85.00	35.00
3	Pepper	Grey-green; yellow rose	75	23.00	30.00	15.00
4	Preserve jar	Mottled green/brown lid; orange/brown pot; orange blackberries; brown leaves	95	80.00	100.00	40.00
5	Salt	Grey-green; yellow rose	75	23.00	30.00	15.00
6	Sugar bowl	Green-brown; orange rose	76	40.00	55.00	30.00

MR. CADDIE SHAPE, 1954-c.1962

When first introduced in mid-1954 the teapot was called the Scottie Teapot because of his tartan hat. The name was changed to Mr. Caddie in November 1954 when a golf bag cream jug and a golf ball sugar bowl were added to boost sales. This shape has also been referred to as "Andy Capp." The teapot was produced with four different coloured tartan hat lids.

Backstamp: A. Gold printed semi-circular "Wade made in England Hand Painted" (1950s)
B. Black ink circular "Royal Victoria Pottery Wade England" (1950-1960)

No.	Description	Colourways	Size	U.S. $	Can. $	U.K. £
1	Cream jug	Cream; orange brown highlighting; silver lustre handle	92	50.00	65.00	32.00
2	Sugar bowl	White	50	30.00	40.00	20.00
3a	Teapot, 4-cup	Creamy brown hat	146	165.00	220.00	125.00
4a	Teapot, 3-cup		133	165.00	220.00	110.00
3b	Teapot, 4-cup	Light green hat	146	165.00	220.00	125.00
4b	Teapot, 3-cup		133	165.00	220.00	110.00
3c	Teapot, 4-cup	Pale blue hat	146	165.00	220.00	125.00
4c	Teapot, 3-cup		133	165.00	220.00	110.00
3d	Teapot, 4-cup	Pale yellow hat	146	165.00	220.00	125.00
4d	Teapot, 3-cup		133	165.00	220.00	110.00

MR CADDIE

OLD ENGLISH CASTLE SHAPE, 1937-1940

O L D

E N G L I S H

Backstamp: Ink stamp "Wade Heath England" with impressed "Old English Castle" (round W 1937-1940)

No.	Description	Colourways	Size	U.S. $	Can. $	U.K. £
1	Biscuit barrel	Yellow; brown turrets/windows/door; green bushes	140 x 140	150.00	200.00	100.00
2	Cheese dish	Yellow; brown turrets/windows/door; green bushes; yellow/brown tray	90 x 175	95.00	130.00	65.00
3	Teapot	Yellow; brown turrets/windows/door; green bushes	130	200.00	260.00	130.00

ORB SHAPE, 1938 - c.1960

STYLE ONE — 1938

Handles:
Version 1 —A dip in the top and three indented dots on the top
Version 2 — No indents
Sugar Bowls:
Version 1 — Open, wide-mouthed and round
Version 2 — Covered, round with moulded half round handles and finial on lid

APPLE BLOSSOM DESIGN

The apple blossom design differs from Style One to Style Two (see page 104).

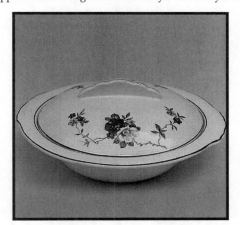

Backstamp: A. Green ink stamp "Wade Heath England"
B. Black ink stamp "Made in England"

No.	Description	Colourways	Size	U.S. $	Can. $	U.K.£
1	Cereal bowl	White; pink/white blossoms; green leaves	37	6.00	8.00	4.00
2	Cream jug, Ver. 2		95	11.00	15.00	8.00
3	Cup and saucer		70/145	7.00	8.00	4.00
4	Dessert serving bowl		220	15.00	20.00	8.00
5	Dessert/soup bowl		165	6.00	8.00	4.00
6	Dinner plate		247	8.00	10.00	5.00
7	Lunch plate		200	8.00	10.00	5.00
8	Milk jug, Ver. 1		95	11.00	15.00	8.00
9	Milk jug, Ver. 2		95	11.00	15.00	8.00
10	Platter, large		355	10.00	13.00	7.00
11	Platter, small		280	8.00	10.00	5.00
12	Sugar bowl, Ver. 2		90	11.00	15.00	8.00
13	Tea plate		153	6.00	7.00	3.00
14	Tureen (vegetable serving dish)		120	22.00	30.00	15.00
15	Teapot, 4-cup		146	50.00	65.00	35.00

ART DECO DESIGN

This set with an Art Deco design of circular broken lines was advertised in 1938 as a tea and dinner service.

Photograph of design
not available
at press time

Backstamp: Green ink stamp "Wade Heath England"

No.	Description	Colourways	Size	U.S. $	Can. $	U.K. £
1	Cream jug, Ver. 2	Cream; green/black lines; green dots	95	9.00	12.00	6.00
2	Cup and saucer		70/145	5.00	7.00	3.00
3	Dinner plate		247	6.00	8.00	4.00
4	Sugar bowl, Ver. 1		90	5.00	7.00	3.00
5	Tea plate		153	5.00	7.00	3.00
6	Teapot, 4-cup		146	40.00	55.00	30.00
7	Tureen (vegetable serving dish)		120	22.00	30.00	15.00

SOLID COLOUR DESIGN

Backstamp: **A.** Ink stamp "Wade Heath England A"
B. Ink stamp "Wade Heath England"

No.	Description	Colourways	Size	U.S. $	Can. $	U.K. £
1	Dessert serving bowl	White	220	8.00	10.00	5.00
2a	Teapot, 2-cup	Off white	115	30.00	40.00	25.00
2b	Teapot, 2-cup	White	115	30.00	40.00	25.00

SPLASH DESIGN

Backstamp: Green ink stamp "Wade Heath England" (round W 1937-1940)

No.	Description	Colourways	Size	U.S. $	Can. $	U.K. £
1	Milk jug, Ver. 2	White; green bands; brown/green splashes	95	9.00	12.00	6.00

ORB

STYLE TWO —c.1948-c.1960

The handles on this style of Orb Ware resemble small elf's ears and have finger grips added to the base. Two new shaped jugs were produced along with a new shaped teapot. Both the jugs and teapot resemble the cups in shape, dipping in at the centre and widening to the top, the finial on the teapot lid was first produced as a ball then changed to a peg shape. Two new sugar bowls matching the cups in shape were also introduced.

      Jugs:
          Version 1 —Footed
          Version 2 — Round and squat
      Sugar Bowls:
          Version 1 — Open sugar bowl
          Version 2 — Covered bowl with a small elf's ear shape handle

APPLE BLOSSOM DESIGN

Backstamp: **A.** Black ink stamp "Wade Heath England A"
               B. Black ink stamp "Wade England"

No.	Description	Colourways	Size	U.S. $	Can. $	U.K. £
1	Cup and saucer	White; pink/white blossoms; brown stems; green leaves	71/142	7.00	8.00	4.00
2	Dessert serving bowl		220	15.00	20.00	8.00
3	Dinner plate		247	7.00	9.00	4.00
4	Lunch plate		200	7.00	9.00	4.00
5	Milk jug, Ver. 1		95	9.00	12.00	6.00
6	Platter, large		355	12.00	10.00	5.00
7	Platter, small		280	12.00	10.00	5.00
8	Sugar bowl, Ver. 2		82	11.00	15.00	8.00
9	Tea plate		163	5.00	7.00	3.00

ORB

AUTUMN LEAVES DESIGN

Backstamp: Green ink stamp "Wade Heath England A" (1939-1945)

No.	Description	Colourways	Size	U.S. $	Can. $	U.K. £
1	Dessert serving bowl	Cream; yellow rim; orange/yellow/ green leaves; small orange yellow flowers	220	12.00	15.00	7.00
2	Platter, large		305	12.00	10.00	5.00

BANDS, NARROW DESIGN

Sugar Bowl, Version 2

Backstamp: Green ink stamp "Wade Heath England A" (c.1948)

No.	Description	Colourways	Size	U.S. $	Can. $	U.K. £
1	Cup and saucer	Cream; orange/yellow bands; silver lines	71/142	12.00	15.00	8.00
2	Sugar bowl, Ver. 2		82	11.00	15.00	8.00
3	Tea plate		153	5.00	7.00	3.00
4	Teapot, 4-cup	White; light brown/pale green/ blue bands	140	40.00	55.00	30.00

ORB

BANDS, WIDE DESIGN

Photograph of design
not available
at press time

Backstamp: Black printed circular "Royal Victoria Pottery Wade England" (c.1952-c.1960)

No.	Description	Colourways	Size	U.S. $	Can. $	U.K. £
1	Cup and saucer	Green/purple/maroon bands	71/146	12.00	15.00	8.00
2	Tea plate		153	5.00	7.00	3.00

BLOSSOM DESIGN

Backstamp: Black ink stamp "Made in England"

No.	Description	Colourways	Size	U.S. $	Can. $	U.K. £
1	Sugar bowl, Ver. 1	Green/orange flowers; grey leaves	74	5.00	7.00	3.00

BRUSH STROKES DESIGN

Backstamp: Green ink stamp "Wade Heath England" (round W 1937-1940)

No.	Description	Colourways	Size	U.S. $	Can. $	U.K. £
1	Breakfast plate	White; green/grey bands and strokes	175	7.00	9.00	4.00
2	Cup and saucer	White; brown bands; brown/green strokes	71/142	12.00	15.00	8.00
3	Cake plate (clipped corners)	White; green/grey bands and strokes	164	10.00	12.00	6.00
4	Tea plate	White; brown bands; brown/green strokes	153	5.00	7.00	3.00

BUTTERFLY CHINTZ DESIGN

This set was first produced in 1939.

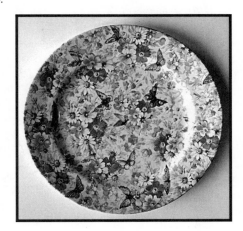

Backstamp: Green ink stamp "Wade Heath England" (round W 1937-c.1940)

No.	Description	Colourways	Size	U.S. $	Can. $	U.K. £
1	Breakfast plate	Creamy yellow; multi-coloured print	175	75.00	100.00	45.00
2	Cake plate, round		222	85.00	112.00	55.00
3	Cream jug, Ver. 1		100	50.00	65.00	30.00
4	Cup and saucer		71/142	75.00	100.00	50.00
5	Sugar bowl, Ver. 1		74	50.00	65.00	30.00
6	Tea plate		153	60.00	80.00	40.00
7	Teapot		140	160.00	212.00	105.00

ORB

CRETONNE

Variation One — Pale Green Bands Design

This design has a pale green band around the border and multi-coloured transfer print of peony, passion and other exotic flowers in the centre.

Photograph of design
not available
at press time

Backstamp: Green ink stamp "Wade England A" (1939-c.1940)

No.	Description	Colourways	Size	U.S. $	Can. $	U.K. £
1	Cup and saucer	White; pale green band; multi-coloured flowers	71/142	12.00	15.00	8.00
2	Dessert serving bowl		220	12.00	15.00	7.00
3	Dinner plate		250	7.00	9.00	4.00
4	Tea plate		153	5.00	7.00	3.00

Variation Two — Gold Bands Design

This design has double backstamps, an ink stamped "Wade England A" and a printed "Wade 'Cretonne' England," which suggests that this set may have been stored and re-issued in the early 1950s with the latest backstamp added.

Backstamp: Green ink stamp "Wade England A" (crossed W c.1945) and a red and green printed "Wade 'Cretonne' England" (c.1954)

No.	Description	Colourways	Size	U.S. $	Can. $	U.K. £
1	Cup and saucer	White; gold bands; multi-coloured flowers	71/142	12.00	15.00	8.00
2	Tea plate		153	5.00	7.00	3.00

FEATHERS DESIGN

Backstamp: **A.** Green ink stamp "Wade Heath England" (round W 1937-1940)
B. Green ink stamp "Wade Heath England A" (c.1948)
C. Green ink stamp "Made In England A" (c.1948)

No.	Description	Colourways	Size	U.S. $	Can. $	U.K. £
1	Breakfast plate	Cream; green/grey bands; green/yellow "feathers"	175	7.00	9.00	4.00
2a	Cup and saucer		71/142	12.00	15.00	8.00
2b	Cup and saucer	Cream; brown/yellow bands; brown/yellow "feathers"	71/142	12.00	15.00	8.00
3	Sugar bowl, Ver. 2	Cream; gold/yellow/brown/green/grey bands; green/yellow "feathers"	82	11.00	15.00	8.00

FLORAL CENTRE AND LACE BAND DESIGN

Backstamp: Printed "Wade England"

No.	Description	Colourways	Size	U.S. $	Can. $	U.K. £
1	Breakfast plate	White; grey lace band; pastel coloured flowers	175	7.00	9.00	4.00
2	Cup and saucer		71/142	12.00	15.00	8.00
3	Dessert serving bowl		220	10.00	15.00	7.00

ORB

FLORAL CENTRE WITH ONE PASTEL BAND DESIGN

This pattern has a pastel yellow band around the rim and pastel flowers in the centre.

Photograph of design
not available
at press time

Backstamp: Printed "Wade England"

No.	Description	Colourways	Size	U.S. $	Can. $	U.K. £
1	Cup and saucer	White; pale yellow band; pastel coloured flowers	71/142	12.00	15.00	8.00

FLORAL CENTRE WITH TWO PASTEL BANDS DESIGN

Backstamp: Printed "Wade England"

No.	Description	Colourways	Size	U.S. $	Can. $	U.K. £
1	Cup and saucer	White; pale green bands; pastel coloured flowers	71/142	10.00	16.00	8.00
2	Tea plate		153	8.00	12.00	6.00
3	Dinner plate		250	10.00	16.00	8.00

FRITILLARY DESIGN

Backstamp: A. Black ink stamp "Wade England" (c.1948-1953)
B. Gold printed circular "Royal Victoria Pottery Wade England" (c.1960-c.1970)

No.	Description	Colourways	Size	U.S. $	Can. $	U.K. £
1	Cup and saucer	White; blue/yellow fritillary flowers; black leaves	71/142	12.00	15.00	8.00

HEDGEROW DESIGN

Backstamp: Printed "Wade 'Hedgerow' England"

No.	Description	Colourways	Size	U.S. $	Can. $	U.K. £
1	Lunch plate	White; blue flowers	200	7.00	9.00	4.00

INDIAN TREE DESIGN

This well-known transfer decoration of a brown tree with large pink flowers was a most popular design of the 1950s-1960s and was an open pattern used for many years by various potteries.

Backstamp: Ink stamped "Wade England" with letter "A" (crossed W c.1945)

No.	Description	Colourways	Size	U.S. $	Can. $	U.K. £
1	Cup and saucer	White; gold band; brown tree; pink flowers	71/142	12.00	15.00	8.00
2	Dessert bowl		165	8.00	11.00	6.00
3	Dinner plate		250	12.00	15.00	8.00
4	Fruit bowl		226	15.00	20.00	10.00
5	Sugar bowl, Ver. 1		74	8.00	11.00	6.00
6	Tea plate		153	8.00	11.00	6.00

LOOPS DESIGN

Backstamp: Green ink stamp "Wade Heath England" (round W 1937-1940)

No.	Description	Colourways	Size	U.S. $	Can. $	U.K. £
1	Breakfast plate	White; green/grey bands/loops	175	7.00	9.00	4.00
2	Cup and saucer		71/142	12.00	15.00	8.00

ORB

MEADOW DESIGN

Backstamp: A. Ink stamp "Wade England" (with or without the pattern name)

No.	Description	Colourways	Size	U.S. $	Can. $	U.K. £
1a	Cup and saucer	White; blue flowers	71/142	12.00	15.00	8.00
2a	Dessert bowl		165	6.00	8.00	4.00
3a	Dinner plate		250	8.00	10.00	5.00
4a	Milk jug, Ver. 2		80	12.00	15.00	7.00
5a	Tea plate		153	6.00	8.00	4.00
1b	Cup and saucer	White; blue, yellow and pink flowers	71/142	12.00	15.00	8.00
2b	Dessert bowl		165	6.00	8.00	4.00
3b	Dinner plate		250	8.00	10.00	5.00
4b	Milk jug, Ver. 2		80	12.00	15.00	7.00
5b	Tea plate		153	6.00	8.00	4.00
1c	Cup and saucer	White; brown, maroon and yellow flowers	71/142	12.00	15.00	8.00
2c	Dessert bowl		165	6.00	8.00	4.00
3c	Dinner plate		250	8.00	10.00	5.00
4c	Milk jug, Ver. 2		80	12.00	15.00	7.00
5c	Tea plate		153	6.00	8.00	4.00
1d	Cup and saucer	White; pink flowers	71/142	12.00	15.00	8.00
2d	Dessert bowl		165	6.00	8.00	4.00
3d	Dinner plate		250	8.00	10.00	5.00
4d	Milk jug, Ver. 2		80	12.00	15.00	7.00
5d	Tea plate		153	6.00	8.00	4.00

POMPADOUR DESIGN

Variation One — With Border of Gold Ribbon Loops and Flowers Design

This plate has the same design as the plates listed below but on this version the border of the plate is decorated with gold ribbon loops and flowers.

Backstamp: Black printed circular "Royal Victoria Pottery Wade England" (c.1952-c.1960)

No.	Description	Colourways	Size	U.S. $	Can. $	U.K. £
1	Cake plate, round	White; multi-coloured print; gold border	164	25.00	35.00	18.00

Variation Two — Without Gold Border Design

This multi-coloured transfer printed design is an open pattern and has been used by other Potteries. Although the Wade Heath version does not have a pattern name on their pieces, "Nelson Ware" of England have the design name "Pompadour" included in their backstamp. The design is a multi-coloured scene of a lady in a lilac and yellow crinoline dress, seated in a cottage garden beside a stone table which is laid for afternoon tea.

Photograph of design
not available
at press time

Backstamp: Black printed circular "Royal Victoria Pottery Wade England" (c.1952-c.1960)

No.	Description	Colourways	Size	U.S. $	Can. $	U.K. £
1	Cup and saucer	White; multi-coloured print	71/142	15.00	18.00	9.00
2	Tea plate		153	10.00	12.00	6.00

POPPY DESIGN

For an illustration
of this design
see page 280

Backstamp: Black printed circular "Royal Victoria Pottery Wade England" (c.1952-c.1960)

No.	Description	Colourways	Size	U.S. $	Can. $	U.K. £
1	Cup and saucer	Salmon pink cup; pinky red poppy flower; pale green/pink leaves	71/142	12.00	15.00	8.00

ORB

POWDERED WARE DESIGN

The glaze of this design is speckled as if dusted with powder hence the name. The outside of the cups are "Powdered" the insides are white as are the centres of the bowls. A twenty piece set of four cups and saucers, oatmeal bowls, four tea plates and lunch plates was advertised in the mid 1950s by a Toronto China store for $4.00 a set. For odd shaped dishes and bowls see pages 374 and 382.

Backstamp: A. Black ink stamp "Wade England" (c.1948-1953)
B. Gold printed circular "Royal Victoria Pottery Wade England" (c.1960-c.1970)

No.	Description	Colourways	Size	U.S. $	Can. $	U.K. £
1a	Cup and saucer	Powdered blue	71/142	8.00	10.00	5.00
2a	Lunch plate		200	7.00	9.00	4.00
3a	Oatmeal bowl		190	6.00	8.00	4.00
4a	Tea plate		153	6.00	8.00	4.00
1b	Cup and saucer	Powdered green	71/142	8.00	10.00	5.00
2b	Lunch plate		200	7.00	9.00	4.00
3b	Oatmeal bowl		190	6.00	8.00	4.00
4b	Tea plate		153	6.00	8.00	4.00
1c	Cup and saucer	Powdered pink	71/142	8.00	10.00	5.00
2c	Lunch plate		200	7.00	9.00	4.00
3c	Oatmeal bowl		190	6.00	8.00	4.00
4c	Tea plate		153	6.00	8.00	4.00
1d	Cup and saucer	Powdered yellow	71/142	8.00	10.00	5.00
2d	Lunch plate		200	7.00	9.00	4.00
3d	Oatmeal bowl		190	6.00	8.00	4.00
4d	Tea plate		153	6.00	8.00	4.00
5	Platter		280	18.00	22.00	11.00

POWDERED WARE WITH DAISY FLOWERS DESIGN

The outside of the cups are powdered and the insides are white with a print of mauve, pink and white daisies near the rim.

Backstamp: Gold printed circular "Royal Victoria Pottery Wade England" (c.1960-c.1970)

No.	Description	Colourways	Size	U.S. $	Can. $	U.K. £
1	Cup and saucer	Powdered green outside; white inside; mauve/pink/white daisies	71/142	12.00	15.00	8.00
2	Lunch plate	Powdered green	200	7.00	9.00	4.00
3	Tea plate		153	7.00	9.00	5.00

ROSETTA DESIGN

It is the gold transfer printed border Rosetta and not the centre design of a pastel pink rose named "Richmond Lass" that gives this set its name. The same pink "Richmond Lass" rose is used on the Regency shaped Cambridge set which again takes its name from the design of the gold border.

Backstamp: Green ink stamp "Wade England" black printed "Wade 'Rosetta' England 5097" in looped frame

No.	Description	Colourways	Size	U.S. $	Can. $	U.K. £
1	Dinner plate	White; gold border; pink Richmond Lass rose; green leaves	250	8.00	10.00	5.00

RUBY ROYAL ROSETTA BORDER, PLAIN CENTRE DESIGN

This design has a wide ruby red band around the rims with a gold Rosetta border, the centre is plain.

For an illustration
of this design
see page 146

Backstamp: Ink stamp "Wade England"

No.	Description	Colourways	Size	U.S. $	Can. $	U.K. £
1	Cup and saucer	White; ruby red band; gold rosetta border	71/142	6.00	8.00	4.00
2	Tea plate		153	6.00	8.00	4.00

SOLID COLOUR DESIGN

Backstamp: Gold printed circular "Royal Victoria Pottery Wade England" (c.1960-c.1970)

No.	Description	Colourways	Size	U.S. $	Can. $	U.K. £
1	Milk jug, Ver. 2	Mottled turquoise	76	10.00	12.00	6.00
2	Sugar bowl, Ver. 1	Off white	82	9.00	12.00	6.00

O
R
B

SPLASH DESIGN

Backstamp: A. Green ink stamp "Wade Heath England" (round W 1937-1940)
B. Black ink stamp "Wade England" (c.1948-1953)

No.	Description	Colourways	Size	U.S. $	Can. $	U.K. £
1b	Breakfast plate	White; grey bands; brown/green splashes	175	7.00	9.00	4.00
1a	Breakfast plate	White; green bands; brown/green splashes	175	7.00	9.00	4.00
2	Cake plate, round	White; brown bands; brown/green splashes	164	10.00	12.00	6.00
3a	Cup and saucer	White; brown bands; brown/yellow splashes	71/142	12.00	15.00	8.00
3b	Cup and saucer	White; green bands; brown/green splashes	71/142	12.00	15.00	8.00
3c	Cup and saucer	White; grey bands; brown/grey splashes	71/142	12.00	15.00	8.00
4	Milk jug, Ver. 2	White; green bands; brown/green splashes	80	12.00	15.00	7.00
5	Teapot, 4-cup	White; brown bands; brown/yellow splashes	140	40.00	55.00	30.00

SPRINGTIME DESIGN

This multi-coloured transfer print of a large parrot tulip and other flowers was used a number of times by Wadeheath on Regency sets (see page 135). Double backstamps indicate that unsold stock was reissued in the 1950s with the current backstamp including the design name added.

For an illustration
of design
see page 135

Backstamp: **A.** Green ink stamp "Wade England A" (crossed W c.1948)
 B. Black printed "Wade 'Springtime' England"

No.	Description	Colourways	Size	U.S. $	Can. $	U.K. £
1	Cup and saucer	White; multi-coloured flowers print	71/142	12.00	15.00	8.00
2	Dinner plate		250	7.00	9.00	4.00
3	Tea plate		153	6.00	8.00	4.00

THISTLE CHINTZ DESIGN

A Thistle design cream jug and sugar bowl were produced in the Dandy shape (see page 52).

Backstamp: **A.** Green ink stamp "Wade Heath England A"
 B. Green ink stamp "Wade England" (crossed W c.1948-1953)

No.	Description	Colourways	Size	U.S. $	Can. $	U.K. £
1	Breakfast plate	Creamy yellow; mauve thistles; yellow gorse; green leaves	175	75.00	100.00	45.00
2	Cup and saucer		71/142	75.00	100.00	50.00
3	Dish, oval		205	75.00	100.00	50.00
4	Tea plate		153	60.00	80.00	40.00

QUEEN SHAPE, c.1927-1937

The hexagonal shaped Queen teapots and jugs have six panels with a high collar neck. The curved handle has a straight top and the teapot finial resembles an acorn. In the late 1920s the teapots could be purchased with either a matching six-footed or round china stand.

CHEQUERED DESIGN

This Queen shape teapot has a gold and black chequered design around the top half and a gold striped bottom half.

Backstamp: Orange ink stamp "Wades England" with lion (1927-1933)

No.	Description	Colourways	Size	U.S. $	Can. $	U.K. £
1	Hot water jug	Gold and black chequered design on top half; white with gold stripes on bottom half	170	50.00	70.00	35.00
2	Stand for teapot		160	35.00	50.00	25.00
3	Teapot, 4-cup		140	100.00	130.00	65.00

CROWN DERBY DESIGN

Variation One — Oval Medallion

Backstamp: A Black ink stamp "Wadeheath England" with lion (1933-1937)
 B. Orange ink stamp "Wades England" with lion (1927-1933)

No.	Description	Colourways	Size	U.S. $	Can. $	U.K. £
1	Hot water jug	Gold neck/ handle; cobalt blue panels with white/ gold decoration on top; white with orange, blue and gold decoration on bottom	170	120.00	160.00	80.00
2	Milk jug, medium		101	65.00	90.00	45.00
3	Stand for teapot	White stand; cobalt blue/orange/gold leaves; gold rim	159	65.00	90.00	45.00
4	Sugar bowl		76	65.00	90.00	45.00
5	Teapot, 6-cup	Gold neck; white/blue/gold spout; cobalt blue panels with white/gold decoration on top; bottom white with orange/blue and gold decoration; spout top half blue/ gold; lower half white with orange leaves	153	135.00	180.00	90.00
6	Teapot, 4-cup		140	135.00	180.00	90.00

QUEEN

Q U E E N

Variation Two — Blue Neck Design, Figure 8 medallion

Backstamp: A Black ink stamp "Wadeheath England" with lion (1933-1937)
    B. Orange ink stamp "Wades England" with lion (1927-1933)

No.	Description	Colourways	Size	U.S. $	Can. $	U.K. £
1	Teapot, 4-cup	Blue neck, handle, spout; cobalt blue panels with white/gold decoration on top; bottom white with orange/blue and gold decoration	140	125.00	165.00	80.00

Variation Three — Striped Background Design

Photograph of this
design not available
at press time

Backstamp: A Black ink stamp "Wadeheath England" with lion (1933-1937)
    B. Orange ink stamp "Wades England" with lion (1927-1933)

No.	Description	Colourways	Size	U.S. $	Can. $	U.K. £
1	Milk jug, large	Gold neck; cobalt blue panels; white/gold decoration on top; bottom white with orange/blue leaves and gold stripe	127	65.00	90.00	45.00
2	Teapot, 4-cup	Gold neck; blue spout/handle; cobalt blue panels; white/gold decoration on top; bottom white with orange/blue leaves and gold stripes; spout blue with gold stripes	140	135.00	180.00	90.00

RAINDROP SHAPE, c.1960 - c.1970

The Irish Wade embossed raindrop design teapot and coffee pot set was very popular during the late 1960s. When the original dies became worn new ones were made which resulted in a variation of the design. For similar shape set but with green shamrock design see Shamrock Range (page 142).

Version One —Pointed Drops Design, c. 1968-1970

Backstamp: **A.** Embossed oval "Irish Porcelain" (over a small shamrock) "Made in Ireland" in Irish knot wreath
              B. Embossed circular "Made in Ireland Porcelain" (central small shamrock and crown) "Wade eire tira dheanta"
Colourways: Blue-grey

No.	Description	Shape No.	Size	U.S. $	Can. $	U.K. £
1	Cream jug	C.311	70	18.00	23.00	12.00
2	Milk jug, 1 pint	C.305	153	30.00	40.00	20.00
3	Milk jug, ¾ pint	C.306	114	22.00	30.00	15.00
4	Milk jug, ½ pint	C.307	101	22.00	30.00	15.00
5	Sugar bowl	C.310	40	15.00	18.00	10.00
6	Teapot	C.312	125	85.00	110.00	50.00
7	Tea strainer	C.309	100	8.00	10.00	5.00

Version Two —Round Drops Design, c. 1960

Backstamp: A. Embossed oval "Irish Porcelain" (over a small Shamrock) "Made in Ireland" in Irish Knot wreath
B. Embossed circular "Made in Ireland Porcelain" (central small shamrock and crown) "Wade eire tira dheanta"
Colourways: Blue-grey

No.	Description	Shape No.	Size	U.S. $	Can. $	U.K. £
1	Cream jug	C.311	70	18.00	23.00	12.00
2	Milk jug, 1 pint	C.305	153	30.00	40.00	20.00
3	Milk jug, ¾ pint	C.306	114	22.00	30.00	15.00
4	Milk jug, ½ pint	C.307	101	22.00	30.00	15.00
5	Sugar bowl	C.310	40	15.00	18.00	10.00
6	Teapot	C.312	125	85.00	110.00	50.00
7	Tea strainer	C.309	100	8.00	10.00	5.00

REGENCY SHAPE, 1952–c.1968

The elegant fluted rib shape of the Regency tablewares is instantly recognized. Gold was a popular decoration on this shape and a number of different types of gold decoration were used.

The Regency sugar bowl was produced in two versions.

Version 1	Covered sugar — Round with looped handles and a lid
Version 2	Open sugar — Narrow at the base and wide at the top

A SOMERSET COTTAGE DESIGN, c.1960

Backstamp: Gold printed circular "Royal Victoria Pottery Wade England" (1960-1970)

No.	Description	Colourways	Size	U.S. $	Can. $	U.K. £
1	Cake plate, chrome handle	White; multi-coloured print; chrome handle	230	22.00	30.00	15.00
2	Cup and saucer		70/145	17.00	22.00	12.00
3	Tea plate		178	12.00	15.00	8.00

CAMBRIDGE DESIGN, c.1955 - c.1962

It is the gold transfer printed border Cambridge and not the centre design of a pastel pink rose named "Richmond Lass" that gives this design its name. The same pink rose is used on the Rosetta set (see page 116).

Backstamp: A. Black printed "Wade Cambridge England" in looped frame
B. Red printed "Wade England"

No.	Description	Colourways	Size	U.S. $	Can. $	U.K. £
1	Cereal/dessert bowl	White; gold border; pink rose; green leaves	130	8.00	10.00	5.00
2	Cup and saucer		70/145	12.00	15.00	8.00
3	Dessert serving bowl		190	20.00	25.00	12.00
4	Dinner plate		255	18.00	22.00	12.00
5	Dish, oval		250	20.00	25.00	12.00
6	Fruit bowl		230	12.00	16.00	8.00
7	Gravy boat/stand	White; gold border	90 x 200	20.00	25.00	12.00
8	Lunch plate	White; gold border; pink rose; green leaves	205	15.00	20.00	10.00
9	Platter, large		367	30.00	40.00	20.00
10	Platter, small		298	25.00	32.00	16.00
11	Sugar bowl, Ver. 1	White; gold border	115	20.00	25.00	12.00
12	Tea plate	White; gold border; pink rose; green leaves	178	10.00	12.00	6.00

CRETONNE DESIGN, c.1948 - 1953

The central design of Cretonne has also been used on the Orb shape (see page 108).

Backstamp: Green ink stamp "Wade England"

No.	Description	Colourways	Size	U.S. $	Can. $	U.K. £
1	Dinner plate	White; pink/yellow flowers on border; multi-coloured flowers in centre	266	18.00	22.00	12.00

DAISIES DESIGN

Backstamp: Unknown

No.	Description	Colourways	Size	U.S. $	Can. $	U.K. £
1	Cup and saucer	Pink; multi-coloured daisy print	70/145	12.00	15.00	8.00
2	Dessert bowl		160	15.00	20.00	10.00
3	Tea plate		178	9.00	12.00	6.00

DOG AND PHEASANT DESIGN

REGENCY

Backstamp: Unknown

No.	Description	Colourways	Size	U.S. $	Can. $	U.K. £
1	Dinner plate	White; brown dog; green grass stems; brown/yellow pheasants	255	18.00	25.00	12.00

GOLD FLOWER CHINTZ DESIGN, c.1960

The round cake plate and the oval sandwich plate both have moulded handles, however the sandwich plate may also be found with a removable chrome handle. This same gold decoration was used on Basket Ware (see page 13).

Backstamp: Gold printed circular "Royal Victoria Pottery Wade England" (1960-1970)
Colourways: White; gold flower/leaf decoration; pink/purple flowers; green leaves

No.	Description	Size	U.S. $	Can. $	U.K. £
1	Cake plate, round, moulded handles	240	25.00	35.00	16.00
2	Cake stand, two tier, chrome handle	230	35.00	45.00	22.00
3	Cream jug	70	20.00	24.00	12.00
4	Cup and saucer	70/145	15.00	20.00	10.00
5	Sandwich plate, oval, chrome handles	285	30.00	40.00	20.00
6	Sugar bowl, Ver. 2	60	10.00	12.00	6.00
7	Tea plate	178	15.00	20.00	10.00

GOLD LUSTRE DESIGN, c.1962

REGENCY

Backstamp: Gold printed circular "Royal Victoria Wade England Pottery" (c.1960-c.1970)

No.	Description	Colourways	Size	U.S. $	Can. $	U.K. £
1	Cup and saucer	Gold	70/145	15.00	20.00	10.00
2	Tea plate		178	12.00	15.00	8.00
3	Teapot, 4-cup		150	45.00	60.00	30.00

HARLECH DESIGN, c.1958-c.1962

Backstamp: Black printed "Wade Harlech England" (c.1958-c.1962)

No.	Description	Colourways	Size	U.S. $	Can. $	U.K. £
1	Cream soup	White; red/blue/yellow flowers; brown leaves	120/160	15.00	20.00	10.00
2	Cup and saucer		70/145	12.00	15.00	8.00
3	Dinner plate		255	18.00	22.00	12.00
4	Tea plate		178	12.00	15.00	8.00

HEDGEROW DESIGN

Backstamp: Printed "Wade Hedgerow England"

No.	Description	Colourways	Size	U.S. $	Can. $	U.K. £
1a	Cup and saucer	Cream; blue flowers	70/145	12.00	15.00	8.00
2a	Dinner plate		255	18.00	22.00	12.00
3a	Tea plate		178	10.00	12.00	6.00
1b	Cup and saucer	Cream; brown flowers	70/145	12.00	15.00	8.00
2b	Dinner plate		255	18.00	22.00	12.00
3b	Tea plate		178	10.00	12.00	6.00
1c	Cup and saucer	Cream; maroon/yellow/blue flowers	70/145	12.00	15.00	8.00
2c	Dinner plate		255	18.00	22.00	12.00
3a	Tea plate		178	10.00	12.00	6.00

INDIAN TREE DESIGN, c.1948 - c.1960

R E G E N C Y

Backstamp: A. Ink stamp "Wade England" (c.1948-1953)
B. Ink stamp "Wade England A"
C. Printed "Gold Circular Royal Victoria Pottery Wade England" (1960-1970)

No.	Description	Colourways	Size	U.S. $	Can. $	U.K. £
1	Cake plate, round, moulded handles	White; brown tree; pink/yellow flowers	240	22.00	30.00	15.00
2	Cream jug		70	18.00	24.00	12.00
3	Cup and saucer		70/145	14.00	18.00	9.00
4	Dinner plate		255	18.00	22.00	12.00
5	Sugar bowl, Ver.1		115	20.00	25.00	12.00
6	Tea plate		178	12.00	15.00	8.00
7	Teapot, 4-cup		150	45.00	60.00	30.00

MEADOW DESIGN, c.1948 - c.1952

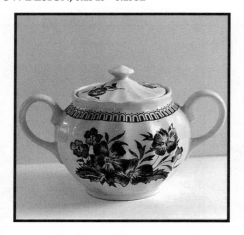 

Backstamp: **A.** Ink stamp "Wade Meadow England"
B. Blue ink stamp "Wade England"
Colourways: **A.** White; blue flowers/leaves
B. White; blue/yellow/pink flowers/leaves
C. White; brown, maroon and yellow flowers; brown leaves
D. Pink flowers and leaves

No.	Description	Size	U.S. $	Can. $	U.K. £
1	Desert bowl	130	8.00	10.00	5.00
2	Dessert serving bowl	190	20.00	25.00	12.00
3	Dinner plate	255	18.00	22.00	12.00
4	Fruit bowl, large	230	12.00	16.00	8.00
5	Lunch plate	205	15.00	20.00	10.00
6	Platter, small	298	30.00	40.00	20.00
7	Sugar bowl, Ver.1	115	20.00	25.00	12.00
8	Tea plate	178	12.00	15.00	8.00
9	Vegetable tureen	248	25.00	35.00	18.00

REGENCY

MOTTLED DESIGN

Only two items have been found to date in this all over one-colour mottled glaze, which is similar to the Flaxman ware decoration seen on decorative wares.

Backstamp: A. Ink stamp "Wade England Flaxman" (c.1948-c.1948)
B. Black ink stamp "Wade England" (crossed W c.1948-1953)

No.	Description	Colourways	Size	U.S. $	Can. $	U.K. £
1a	Fruit bowl, small	White	180	28.00	35.00	18.00
1b	Fruit bowl, small	Yellow	180	28.00	35.00	18.00
2	Sugar bowl, Ver. 2	Pale green	60	8.00	10.00	5.00

POMPADOUR DESIGN, c.1960

This transfer printed design is an open pattern and has been used by other Potteries. Although the Wade Heath version does not have a pattern name, Nelson Ware of England call the design "Pompadour." The design is a multi-coloured scene of a lady in a lilac crinoline dress, seated in a cottage garden beside a stone table which is laid for afternoon tea. The rims are decorated with a gold Fleur-de-Lis border. The cake plate has a chrome and bakerlite handle in the middle which is fixed by a screw through a central hole.

An illustration of this
design can be seen
on page 114

Backstamp: Black printed circular "Royal Victoria Pottery Wade England" (c.1952-c.1960)

No.	Description	Colourways	Size	U.S. $	Can. $	U.K. £
1	Cake plate, chrome handle	White; multi-coloured print	240	22.00	30.00	15.00
2	Cup and saucer		70/145	14.00	18.00	9.00
3	Tea plate		178	15.00	20.00	10.00

REGENCY

SOUVENIRS DESIGN, 1960

Canada Design

Many souvenir items were produced for the British Colonies, mostly tankards and dishes.

Photograph of this
design not available
at press time

Backstamp: Gold printed circular "Royal Victoria Pottery Wade England" (c.1960-c.1975)

No.	Description	Colourways	Size	U.S. $	Can. $	U.K. £
1	Cup and saucer	Cup - white; red lobster print; black lettering "Nova Scotia," Saucer - white	67/140	14.00	18.00	9.00

Great Britain Design

Dish, Windsor Castle

Cream Jug, Balmoral Castle

Backstamp: Gold printed circular "Royal Victoria Pottery Wade England" (c.1960-c.1975)

No.	Description	Colourways	Size	U.S. $	Can. $	U.K. £
1	Cream jug	White; multi-coloured print, Balmoral Castle	82	22.00	30.00	15.00
2a	Cup and saucer	White; multi-coloured print, Balmoral Castle	70/145	20.00	25.00	12.00
2b	Cup and saucer	Off-white; multi-coloured print, Windsor Castle	70/145	20.00	25.00	12.00
3	Dish	White; multi-coloured print, Windsor Castle	101	15.00	20.00	10.00
4	Sugar bowl, Ver. 2	White; multi-coloured print, Balmoral Castle	60	15.00	20.00	10.00
5	Tea plate	Off-white; multi-coloured print, Windsor Castle	178	15.00	20.00	10.00

REGENCY

SPRINGTIME DESIGN

Backstamp: Black printed "Wade Springtime England" in frame

No.	Description	Colourways	Size	U.S. $	Can. $	U.K. £
1	Sandwich plate, oval moulded handles	White; pale green edging; multi-coloured print	285	30.00	40.00	20.00

SAMANTHA SHAPE, 1988-1994

CHATSWORTH EXOTIC FLOWER DESIGN, 1993

Backstamp: Printed "Wade England" between two lines

No.	Description	Colourways	Size	U.S. $	Can. $	U.K. £
1a	Mug	White; dusky rose/pale green exotic flowers and leaves	95	3.00	4.00	2.00
1b	Mug	White; dusky rose band; dusky rose/pale green exotic flowers and leaves	95	3.00	4.00	2.00
2	Teapot, 6-cup	Ivory; dusky rose/pale green exotic flowers and leaves	177	25.00	35.00	18.00

CHATSWORTH MINIATURE FLOWER DESIGN

Backstamp: Printed "Wade England" between two lines

No.	Description	Colourways	Size	U.S. $	Can. $	U.K. £
1	Mug	White; miniature dusky rose flowers; dusky rose band with exotic flowers around base	95	3.00	4.00	2.00
2	Teapot, 6-cup	Ivory; miniature dusky rose flowers	177	25.00	35.00	18.00

FRUITS DESIGN, 1992

Extra large cups and saucers were produced to match the "Samantha Fruits" teapots. The saucers have been found in white, dark green or white with a band of leaves around the rim.

Backstamp: Printed "Wade England" between two lines

No.	Description	Colourways	Size	U.S. $	Can. $	U.K. £
1	Cream jug	White; strawberries	95	12.00	15.00	8.00
2a	Cup and saucer	White; red apples; green leaves	88/195	12.00	15.00	8.00
2b	Cup and saucer	White; brambles; green leaves	88/195	12.00	15.00	8.00
2c	Cup and saucer	White; red/yellow cherries; green leaves	88/195	12.00	15.00	8.00
2d	Cup and saucer	White; purple plums; green leaves	88/195	12.00	15.00	8.00
3	Sugar bowl	White; strawberries	70	10.00	12.00	6.00
4a	Teapot, 4-cup	White; red apples; green leaves	140	25.00	30.00	18.00
4b	Teapot, 4-cup	White; brambles; green leaves	140	25.00	30.00	18.00
4c	Teapot, 4-cup	White; red/yellow cherries; green leaves	140	25.00	30.00	18.00
4d	Teapot, 4-cup	White; purple plums; green leaves	140	25.00	30.00	18.00

S
A
M
A
N
T
H
A

WILD FLOWERS DESIGN, 1991-1994

S A M A N T H A

Backstamp: Red printed "Wade England" between two lines

No.	Description	Colourways	Size	U.S. $	Can. $	U.K. £
1	Cream jug	White; multi-coloured print bellflowers	95	10.00	12.00	6.00
2	Gravy jug/stand	White; multi-coloured print pimpernels	unknown	10.00	12.00	6.00
3	Sugar bowl	White; multi-coloured print California poppies	70	6.00	8.00	4.00

SELBY SHAPE, c.1927-1933

This shape was first advertised in *The Pottery and Glass Trades Review* in February 1930. For additional Shelby items see pages 224-225 in the teapot section and page 323 in the jug section.

FERN LEAVES AND LARGE GOLD FLOWERS DESIGN

Backstamp: A. Orange ink stamp "Wades England" with lion (c.1927-1933)
B. Impressed "Made in England"

No.	Description	Colourways	Size	U.S. $	Can. $	U.K. £
1	Hot water jug, metal lid	Black; gold bands, flower, fern leaves; large gold flowers; yellow/green leaves	159	85.00	110.00	60.00
2	Stand for teapot		165	40.00	50.00	25.00
3	Teapot		133	85.00	110.00	60.00

S E L B Y

FERN LEAVES AND SMALL PINK FLOWERS DESIGN

Backstamp: A. Orange ink stamp "Wades England" with lion (c.1927-1933)
B. Impressed "Made in England"

No.	Description	Colourways	Size	U.S. $	Can. $	U.K. £
1	Hot water jug	Black; gold bands, flower, fern leaves; small pink flowers; yellow/green leaves	159	85.00	110.00	60.00
2	Stand for teapot		165	40.00	50.00	25.00
3	Teapot		133	85.00	110.00	60.00

FORGET-ME-NOTS DESIGN

Backstamp: Orange ink stamp "Wades England" with lion (c.1927-1933)

No.	Description	Colourways	Size	U.S. $	Can. $	U.K. £
1	Hot water jug	Buff; blue flowers; green leaves and tendrils; mottled blue band	159	125.00	150.00	75.00
2	Stand for teapot	Buff; blue flowers; green leaves and tendrils	165	55.00	70.00	35.00
3	Teapot	Buff; blue flowers; green leaves and tendrils; mottled blue band	133	135.00	160.00	85.00

SHAMROCK RANGE, 1983-1986

The shape of this set is the same as the Raindrop tea set (page 123) but without an embossed design.

Backstamp: Unknown
Colourways: White; green shamrocks

No.	Description	Shape No.	Size	U.S. $	Can. $	U.K. £
1	Coffee cup	SR.08	63	15.00	20.00	10.00
2	Coffee pot	SR.04	159	60.00	80.00	40.00
3	Cream jug	SR.06	83	15.00	20.00	10.00
4	Salt and pepper	SR.07	63	15.00	20.00	10.00
5	Sugar bowl	SR.06	62	12.00	15.00	8.00
6	Teapot	SR.05	120	60.00	80.00	40.00

STANDARD SHAPE

Wade Standard shapes were a mixture of shapes, for example Flair shape cups with Orb shape handles. Standard shapes were decorated with the same designs as used on the Shaped sets.

APPLE BLOSSOM DESIGN

Backstamp: Black ink stamp "Wade England"

No.	Description	Colourways	Size	U.S. $	Can. $	U.K. £
1	Cereal bowl	White; pink/white blossoms; brown stems; green leaves	37	6.00	8.00	4.00
2	Dessert serving bowl		203	15.00	20.00	8.00
3	Sauce boat/stand		224	20.00	25.00	12.00

BANDED DESIGN

Backstamp: Black ink stamp "Wade England"

No.	Description	Colourways	Size	U.S. $	Can. $	U.K. £
1	Cup and saucer	Green/purple/maroon bands	73/140	12.00	16.00	8.00
2	Tea plate		153	9.00	12.00	6.00

S T A N D A R D

CRETONNE DESIGN

Backstamp: Printed "Wade 'Cretonne' England" (c.1952)

No.	Description	Colourways	Size	U.S. $	Can. $	U.K. £
1	Dessert serving bowl	White; gold bands; multi-coloured flowers	190	12.00	15.00	7.00
2	Dinner plate		250	7.00	9.00	4.00
3	Jug		220	9.00	12.00	6.00
4	Lunch plate		220	7.00	9.00	4.00
5	Platter, small		298	12.00	10.00	5.00
6	Sauce boat/stand		220	20.00	25.00	12.00
7	Tea plate		195	5.00	7.00	3.00
8	Vegetable tureen		135 x 245	22.00	30.00	15.00

DAISIES DESIGN, 1953 - c.1962

Backstamp: Impressed "England" and red printed "Wade England"

No.	Description	Colourways	Size	U.S. $	Can. $	U.K. £
1	Cup and saucer	Cup - outer, dusky rose with gold rim; inner, white with multi-coloured print Saucer - white; gold rim; multi-coloured print	73/140	12.00	15.00	8.00
2	Tea plate	White; gold rim; multi-coloured print	160	9.00	12.00	6.00

STANDARD

MAUVANA DESIGN, c.1948

This mixed set, advertised as "Mauvana," consists of a Nelson teapot, a tea plate, Dandy milk and cream jugs and sugar bowls.

Backstamp: Green ink stamp "Wade Heath England" (crossed W c.1948-1953)

No.	Description	Colourways	Size	U.S. $	Can. $	U.K. £
1	Cream jug	Cream; mauve/yellow flowers; green/brown leaves	88	25.00	35.00	15.00
2	Milk jug		140	25.00	35.00	18.00
3	Sugar bowl		50	20.00	25.00	12.00
4	Tea plate		172	15.00	20.00	10.00
5	Teapot		140	90.00	120.00	60.00

ORCHID DESIGN, 1953 - c.1962

Backstamp: Impressed "England" and red printed "Wade England"

No.	Description	Colourways	Size	U.S. $	Can. $	U.K. £
1	Cup and saucer	Cup - outer, dusky; inner, white; pink print Saucer - white; pink print	73/140	12.00	15.00	8.00
2	Tea plate	White; pink print	160	9.00	12.00	6.00

RUBY ROYAL ROSETTA BORDER, PLAIN CENTRE DESIGN, c.1948 - 1953

A green ink Wade England backstamp over lapped by a printed Wade Ruby Royal England backstamp indicates that this set was originally produced c.1948 and unsold stock was reissued in the 1950s with the current backstamp and design name added.

Backstamp: **A.** Green ink stamp "Wade England" (crossed W c.1948)
B. Printed "Wade Ruby Royal England"

No.	Description	Colourways	Size	U.S. $	Can. $	U.K. £
1	Cup and saucer	White; ruby red band; gold rosetta border	55	10.00	12.00	6.00
2	Dinner plate		248	6.00	7.00	3.00
3	Fruit bowl		225	6.00	7.00	3.00
4	Platter, large		360	10.00	12.00	5.00
5	Vegetable tureen		245	15.00	20.00	10.00

S T A N D A R D

RUBY ROYAL DESIGN WITH RICHMOND LASS ROSE CENTRE DESIGN, c.1948 - c.1958

This design has a wide ruby red band around the edges and has the same pink rose, "Richmond Lass" as on the Rosetta and Cambridge tablewares. The cup is Flair shape but the handle is Orb shape. First produced just after World War II, unsold stock was re-issued c.1958 with the current backstamp and design name added.

Backstamp: **A.** Green ink stamp "Wade England" (crossed W c.1948)
B. Green ink stamp "Wade England" and black printed "Wade Royal Victoria England" (c.1958)

No.	Description	Colourways	Size	U.S. $	Can. $	U.K. £
1	Cup and saucer	White; ruby red band; pink rose	55/195	12.00	15.00	8.00
2	Dinner plate		250	18.00	22.00	12.00
3	Platter, large		360	30.00	40.00	20.00
4	Platter, medium		316	30.00	40.00	20.00
5	Sauce boat/stand		220	20.00	25.00	12.00
6	Soup tureen		245	22.00	30.00	15.00

TUTTI FRUTTI SHAPE, 1991 - 1995

A set — consisting of a teapot (6-cup), cream jug and sugar bowl — with an embossed design of fruits was produced from 1991-1993 in seven colourways. A butter dish, cheese dish, cup and saucer, mug, plate and storage jars were produced in five of these colours. In 1993 five new items were added to the set — a milk jug, salt and pepper pots, fruit bowl and a small teapot (2-cup) — and was only produced in ivory with multi-coloured hand-painted fruits.

BLUE DESIGN

Backstamp: Embossed "Wade England"

No.	Description	Colourways	Size	U.S. $	Can. $	U.K. £
1	Butter dish	Blue	114	40.00	52.00	30.00
2	Cheese dish		114	45.00	60.00	35.00
3	Cream jug		85	25.00	30.00	15.00
4	Cup and saucer		88/140	25.00	30.00	15.00
5	Lunch plate		205	25.00	30.00	15.00
6	Mug		101	18.00	25.00	12.00
7	Storage jar, large		205	40.00	45.00	30.00
8	Storage jar, medium		184	30.00	35.00	25.00
9	Sugar bowl		101	25.00	35.00	18.00
10	Teapot, 6-cup		160	60.00	80.00	40.00

BURGUNDY DESIGN

Backstamp: A. Embossed "Wade England"
      B. Printed "Wade England" with two lines

No.	Description	Colourways	Size	U.S. $	Can. $	U.K. £
1	Cream jug	Burgundy	85	25.00	30.00	15.00
2	Sugar bowl		101	25.00	35.00	18.00
3	Teapot, 6-cup		160	60.00	80.00	40.00

CREAM DESIGN

Photograph of this
colourway not available
at press time

Backstamp: Printed "Wade England" with two lines

No.	Description	Colourways	Size	U.S. $	Can. $	U.K. £
1	Cream jug	Cream	85	25.00	30.00	15.00
2	Sugar bowl		101	25.00	35.00	18.00
3	Teapot, 6-cup		160	60.00	80.00	40.00

DARK GREEN DESIGN

This colourway was produced for Boots the Chemist in 1993.

T
U
T
T
I

F
R
U
T
T
I

Backstamp: A. Embossed "Wade England"
              B. Printed "Wade England" with two lines

No.	Description	Colourways	Size	U.S. $	Can. $	U.K. £
1	Cup and saucer	Dark green	80/104	25.00	30.00	15.00

HONEY DESIGN

Backstamp: Embossed "Wade England"

No.	Description	Colourways	Size	U.S. $	Can. $	U.K. £
1	Cream jug	Honey	85	25.00	30.00	15.00
2	Storage jar, large		205	40.00	45.00	30.00
3	Storage jar, medium		184	30.00	35.00	25.00
4	Sugar bowl		101	25.00	35.00	18.00
5	Teapot, 6-cup		160	60.00	80.00	40.00

IF YOU OWN THIS BOOK YOU SHOULD BELONG TO THIS CLUB

THE OFFICIAL INTERNATIONAL WADE COLLECTORS CLUB

In 1994 The Official International Wade Collectors Club was founded to offer the Wade Collector information, support and an insight into the world of Wade, without which it would be impossible to build a meaningful collection.

ANNUAL MEMBERSHIP FIGURE

New each year, these exclusive annual membership figures become collector items in their own right. "The Wade Baby" is the membership model for the 1997-1998 year.

MEMBERSHIP CERTIFICATE

Every new member receives a personalised membership certificate on joining.

WADE'S WORLD MAGAZINE

This quarterly full-colour club magazine is packed with information on limited editions, club news, Wade fairs and events and "wanted" and "for sale" adverts.

CLUB LIMITED EDITIONS

Only club members can participate in purchasing the various club limited edition figures which are offered every year.

ANNUAL MEMBERSHIP PIN

Each year a new collector's pin is included free with membership. The 1998 collector's pin features "The Wade Baby."

Royal Works, Westport Road, Burslem,
Stoke-on-Trent, ST6 4AP England
In UK: Tel 01782 255255   Fax 01782 575195
Overseas: Tel 44 1782 255255   Fax 44 1782 575195

MEMBERSHIP OPTIONS

ANNUAL INDIVIDUAL MEMBERSHIP
(12 months from receipt of application)
UK Membership £18
Overseas Membership £23 or $36 US

ANNUAL FAMILY MEMBERSHIP
(12 months from receipt of application)
UK Membership £60
Overseas Membership £78 or $120 US

A family of 4 can enjoy full membership benefits. This is offered for up to four people, any additional family members will be charged at full rate, no reduction for families of less than four. All family memberships must enrol on one application form and all memberships will commence from the same month

TWO YEAR MEMBERSHIP
(24 months from receipt of application)
UK Membership £32
Overseas Membership £42 or $66 US

Receive a special bonus price when you join for two years. You will receive your current years membership piece on receipt of your application and on the anniversary of your membership, you will automatically receive your second piece.

ENROL A FRIEND

The "Enrol a Friend" scheme is available when you introduce a new member for a 1 year membership. Your friend will enjoy all the benefits of club membership plus you will both be sent a BONUS GIFT.

MEMBERSHIP APPLICATION FORM

Please enrol me/my family/my friend as a member(s):

Title . . . . . First Name . . . . Last Name . . . .

Address . . . .

. . . .

. . . .

Post/Zip Code . . . . Telephone Number . . . .

☐ My cheque for . . . . made to payable to Wade Ceramics Limited is enclosed
(cheques are accepted in Pounds Sterling and US Dollars)

☐ Debit my credit/charge card ☐ Visa ☐ Access ☐ American Express the sum of _____

Card No. ☐☐☐☐☐☐☐☐☐☐☐☐☐☐☐☐☐☐ Expiry ☐☐☐☐

Other 3 Family Names (for family membership): . . . .
. . . .

Enrol a Friend and Both Receive a Bonus Gift

Title . . . . . First Name . . . . Last Name . . . .

Address . . . .

. . . .

. . . .

Post/Zip Code . . . . Telephone Number . . . .

My Membership Number . . . .

Friends Signature . . . . Date . . . .

I am/am not a member of the Jim Beam Bottle Club _____ Number

Send to:

THE OFFICIAL INTERNATIONAL WADE COLLECTORS CLUB
Wade Ceramics Limited
Royal Works, Westport Road, Burslem, Stoke-on-Trent, ST6 4AP England
In UK: Tel 01782 255255   Fax 01782 575195
From Overseas: Tel 44 1782 255255   Fax 44 1782 575195

IVORY DESIGN

Photograph of this
colourway not available
at press time

Backstamp: Printed "Wade England" with two lines

No.	Description	Colourways	Size	U.S. $	Can. $	U.K. £
1	Butter dish	Ivory	114	40.00	52.00	30.00
2	Cheese dish		114	45.00	60.00	35.00
3	Cream jug		85	25.00	30.00	15.00
4	Cup and saucer		88/140	25.00	30.00	15.00
5	Lunch plate		205	25.00	30.00	15.00
6	Mug		101	18.00	25.00	12.00
7	Storage jar, large		205	40.00	45.00	30.00
8	Storage jar, medium		184	30.00	35.00	25.00
9	Sugar bowl		101	25.00	35.00	18.00
10	Teapot, 6-cup		160	60.00	80.00	40.00

IVORY, MULTI-COLOURED FRUITS DESIGN

Backstamp: Printed "Wade England" with two lines

No.	Description	Colourways	Size	U.S. $	Can. $	U.K. £
1	Butter dish	Ivory, multi-coloured fruits	114	50.00	70.00	35.00
2	Cheese dish		114	55.00	75.00	40.00
3	Cream jug		85	40.00	50.00	25.00
4	Cup and saucer		88/140	30.00	35.00	20.00
5	Fruit bowl		229	55.00	75.00	38.00
6	Lunch plate		205	35.00	45.00	25.00
7	Milk jug		140	45.00	60.00	30.00
8	Mug		101	18.00	25.00	12.00
9	Pepper		76	10.00	15.00	8.00
10	Salt		76	10.00	15.00	8.00
11	Storage jar, large		205	50.00	65.00	35.00
12	Storage jar, medium		184	45.00	60.00	30.00
13	Sugar bowl		101	35.00	45.00	22.00
14	Teapot, 6-cup		160	70.00	90.00	45.00
15	Teapot, 2-cup		127	50.00	70.00	35.00

TUTTI FRUTTI

PINK DESIGN

Backstamp: Printed "Wade England" with two lines

No.	Description	Colourways	Size	U.S. $	Can. $	U.K. £
1	Cream jug	Pink	85	25.00	30.00	15.00
2	Sugar bowl		101	25.00	35.00	18.00
3	Teapot, 4-cup		160	60.00	80.00	40.00

ROCKINGHAM BROWN DESIGN

Photograph of this
colourway not available
at press time

Backstamp: Printed "Wade England" with two lines

No.	Description	Colourways	Size	U.S. $	Can. $	U.K. £
1	Butter dish	Brown	114	40.00	52.00	30.00
2	Cheese dish		114	45.00	60.00	35.00
3	Cream jug		85	25.00	30.00	15.00
4	Cup and saucer		88/140	25.00	30.00	15.00
5	Lunch plate		205	25.00	30.00	15.00
6	Mug		101	18.00	25.00	12.00
7	Storage jar, medium		184	30.00	35.00	25.00
8	Storage jar, large		205	40.00	45.00	30.00
9	Sugar bowl		101	25.00	35.00	18.00
10	Teapot, 4-cup		160	60.00	80.00	40.00

VICTORIA SHAPE, 1986 - 1994

CHARLOTTE DESIGN, 1988 - 1994

For an illustration
of this design
see page 222

Backstamp: Printed "Charlotte Wade England"

No.	Description	Colourways	Size	U.S. $	Can. $	U.K. £
1	Cream jug	White; small pink/yellow flowers; green leaves	95	6.00	8.00	4.00
2	Coffee pot		140	25.00	35.00	18.00
3	Sugar bowl		95	5.00	7.00	3.00
4	Teapot, 2-cup		140	25.00	35.00	18.00

COUNTRY BLUE DESIGN, 1984 - 1994

Backstamp: Printed "Wade" with two lines

No.	Description	Colourways	Size	U.S. $	Can. $	U.K. £
1	Cream jug	White; blue country scene	95	6.00	8.00	4.00
2	Sugar bowl		95	5.00	7.00	3.00
3	Teapot, 4-cup		165	28.00	38.00	20.00
4	Teapot, 2-cup		140	25.00	35.00	18.00

VICTORIA

FLORAL RHAPSODY DESIGN, 1984 - 1994

VICTORIA

Backstamp: Printed "Floral Rhapsody Wade England"

No.	Description	Colourways	Size	U.S. $	Can. $	U.K. £
1	Cream jug	White; band of pink flowers; grey leaves	95	6.00	8.00	4.00
2	Sugar bowl		95	5.00	7.00	3.00
3	Teapot, 4- cup		165	28.00	38.00	20.00
4	Teapot, 2-cup		140	25.00	35.00	18.00

MARIGOLDS DESIGN, 1991 - 1994

This design is of a spray of small orange and yellow flowers resembling marigolds in the centre and a band of flowers around the rims.

Photograph of this
decoration not available
at press time

Backstamp: Red printed "Wade England" between two lines

No.	Description	Colourway	Size	U.S. $	Can. $	U.K. £
1	Cream jug	White; multi-coloured print	95	6.00	8.00	4.00
2	Sugar bowl		95	5.00	7.00	3.00

ROSE DESIGN, 1988 - 1989

Backstamp: Printed "Rose Wade England"

No.	Description	Colourways	Size	U.S. $	Can. $	U.K. £
1	Coffee pot	White; large pink roses; green leaves	140	25.00	35.00	18.00
2	Cream jug		95	6.00	8.00	4.00
3	Sugar bowl		95	5.00	7.00	3.00
4	Teapot, 2-cup		140	25.00	35.00	18.00

WILD FLOWERS DESIGN, 1991 - 1994

Creeping Jenny Design

Backstamp: Red printed " Wade England" between two lines

No.	Description	Colourways	Size	U.S. $	Can. $	U.K. £
1	Cream jug	White; creeping jenny and pimpernel print	95	10.00	15.00	8.00
2	Sugar bowl		75	10.00	15.00	8.00
3	Tea caddy		150	18.00	25.00	12.00

Daisies and Dandelions Design

Backstamp: Red printed " Wade England" between two lines

No.	Description	Colourways	Size	U.S. $	Can. $	U.K. £
1	Cream jug	White; daisies and dandelion print	95	10.00	15.00	8.00
2	Sugar bowl		75	10.00	15.00	8.00
3	Tea caddy		150	18.00	25.00	12.00

Knapweed Design

Backstamp: Red printed " Wade England" between two lines

No.	Description	Colourways	Size	U.S. $	Can. $	U.K. £
1	Cream jug	White; knapweed print	95	10.00	15.00	8.00
2	Sugar bowl		75	10.00	15.00	8.00
3	Tea caddy		150	18.00	25.00	12.00

VICTORIA

UNKNOWN SHAPES

The following items have only a design name as no shape name has been found at time of writing.

ASSORTED DESIGNS

There are two versions of finial to be found on this shape. One version is round with a button on the top the other finial is flat on two sides with a button on the top (these are probably replacement lids). The teapot is similar in shape and size to the Nelson teapots, and the jugs can be confused with Selby jugs. The round biscuit barrel has no handle.

| Teapot 4a | Teapot 4b | Teapot 4c |

Backstamp: Orange ink stamp "Wades England" with lion and impressed England (1927-1933)

No.	Description	Colourways	Size	U.S. $	Can. $	U.K. £
1	Biscuit barrel	Cobalt blue; gold bands/dots	127	45.00	70.00	35.00
2	Hot water jug	Royal blue; gold design	185	120.00	160.00	85.00
3	Stand for teapot	Powder blue centre; white band with small blue, pink, yellow flowers; gold dots	159	35.00	45.00	25.00
4a	Teapot	White; multi-coloured print of cottage and garden; gold dots; black lettering; "A bit of old England"	140	115.00	150.00	75.00
4b	Teapot	White; multi-coloured print of flying duck/pond/ bulrushes	140	115.00	150.00	75.00
4c	Teapot	White; orange marigolds; green leaves	140	85.00	110.00	65.00
4d	Teapot	Powder blue; white band with small blue, pink, yellow flowers; gold dots	140	115.00	150.00	75.00

COCKEREL DESIGN, c.1938 - c.1940

Designed by Robert Barlow of Quack-Quacks fame, this pretty hand-painted combination set has a pink crowing cockerel with the rays of the sun around him. The shape of the cup is Flair which was later introduced as a new shape in 1953, but the handle is ear shaped as on the 1938 Orb cups. The sugar bowl and cream jug are the popular Dandy shape.

Backstamp: Green ink stamp "Wade Heath England A" (rounded W 1937-1940)

No.	Description	Colourways	Size	U.S. $	Can. $	U.K. £
1	Breakfast plate	White with green edging; pink/green cockerel; yellow sun rays; green grass	205	25.00	35.00	18.00
2	Cream jug		74	30.00	40.00	20.00
3	Cup and saucer		56/141	25.00	35.00	18.00
4	Cereal bowl		153	15.00	20.00	10.00
5	Egg cup		96	12.00	15.00	8.00
6	Sugar bowl		55	15.00	20.00	10.00
7	Tea plate		163	15.00	20.00	10.00

CROWN DERBY DESIGN

There are two different unknown shapes which are decorated with the Crown Derby design.

Variation One

This design (pattern Nos 1624 and 1629) has a cobalt blue banded top with a gold and orange figure eight shaped medallion in the centre of the band. The base design has three oranges on solid blue leaves with gold edging and the background is orange and gold squiggles. Teapot spouts are blue with one gold stripe.

Backstamp: A. Orange ink stamp "Wades England" with lion
B. Black ink stamp "Wadeheath England" with lion
C. Black ink stamp "Wadeheath Ware England"

No.	Description	Colourways	Size	U.S. $	Can. $	U.K. £
1	Biscuit barrel	White; cobalt blue/orange/blue/gold decoration	177	75.00	100.00	50.00
2	Cream jug		65	45.00	60.00	30.00
3	Cup and saucer		70/146	25.00	35.00	18.00
4	Fruit bowl		82	75.00	100.00	50.00
5	Tea plate		146	40.00	50.00	25.00
6	Sandwich plate, rectangular		350	50.00	70.00	35.00
7	Sugar bowl		57	25.00	35.00	18.00
8	Teapot, 4-cup		146	125.00	170.00	85.00
9	Teapot, 2-cup		110	125.00	170.00	85.00

Variation Two

This design (pattern Nos 1624 and 1629) has a cobalt blue banded top with a gold and orange figure eight shaped medallion in the centre of the band, gold curls surround the medallion. The base design has three oranges on solid blue leaves with gold edging and the background is orange and gold squiggles. Teapot spouts are blue with one gold stripe.

Backstamp: Orange ink stamp "Wades England" with lion (1927-1933)

No.	Description	Colourways	Size	U.S. $	Can. $	U.K. £
1	Hot water jug, metal lid	White; cobalt blue/orange/blue/gold decoration	159	140.00	180.00	90.00
2	Milk jug		unknown	80.00	110.00	55.00
3	Sugar bowl		90	60.00	80.00	40.00
4	Teapot		114	140.00	180.00	90.00

CURLED KNOT HANDLES DESIGN, 1937-1940

The handles of the cup, jug and cake plate have a curled knot in the top where it joins the body. A coffee set with the same shape handles has also been found (see page 285).

DAISIES DESIGN

The design on this cup and saucer is of daisy flowers.

Photograph of this
decoration not available
at press time

Backstamp: Black or green ink stamp "Wade Heath England" (round W 1937-c.1948)

No.	Description	Colourways	Size	U.S. $	Can. $	U.K. £
1	Cup and saucer	Cream; purple/maroon daisies; green/brown leaves	63/146	12.00	15.00	8.00

LOOPS DESIGN

The design on this set is of thin loops and crosses.

Backstamp: **A.** Black or green ink stamp "Wade Heath England" (round W 1937-c.1948)
B. Embossed "England"

No.	Description	Colourways	Size	U.S. $	Can. $	U.K. £
1	Cake plate	Cream; brown/grey loops	254	25.00	35.00	18.00
2	Cup and saucer		70/130	12.00	15.00	8.00
3	Milk jug		85	12.00	15.00	8.00
4	Sugar bowl		63	10.00	12.00	6.00
5	Tea plate		146	10.00	12.00	6.00

MOTTLED BLUE DESIGN, 1927-1933

Backstamp: A. Orange ink stamp "Wades England" with lion and impressed "England" (1927-1933)
B. Black ink stamp "Wadeheath Ware England" (1934-1937)

No.	Description	Colourways	Size	U.S. $	Can. $	U.K. £
1	Cream jug	Off white; purple rim; purple/orange flowers; green leaves; mottled blue base	90	25.00	40.00	20.00
2	Sugar bowl		90	25.00	40.00	20.00

POWDERED BLUE DESIGN, 1927-1933

This pretty design is of powdered blue (this type of speckled decoration was later used on the Orb Tablewares) with multi-coloured prints of flowers on a white band, the embossed dots are highlighted in gold.

Photograph of design
not available
at press time

Backstamp: Orange ink stamp "Wades England" with lion (1927-1933)

No.	Description	Colourways	Size	U.S. $	Can. $	U.K. £
1	Stand for teapot	Powdered blue; gold embossed dots; white band; multi-coloured flowers print	159	45.00	60.00	30.00
2	Teapot		159	55.00	65.00	35.00

SEAGOE CERAMICS, 1990-1993

These modern sets were all produced in the same shape and were available in six colourful transfer printed designs, although they are backstamped Wade England they were all produced in the Wade Ireland Seagoe Ceramics Pottery.

BLUE "CHINTZ" DESIGN

This set was available in both a pink and a blue colourway. See page 167 for Rose Chintz.

Backstamp: Printed "Wade England" with two lines

No.	Description	Colourways	Size	U.S. $	Can. $	U.K. £
1	Coffee cup and saucer	White; blue flowers	57/140	8.00	10.00	5.00
2	Coffee pot		229	35.00	45.00	22.00
3	Cream jug		95	6.00	8.00	4.00
4	Cup and saucer		60/171	8.00	10.00	5.00
5	Gravy jug		82	6.00	8.00	4.00
6	Lunch plate		229	9.00	12.00	6.00
7	Pepper		80	5.00	6.00	3.00
8	Salt		80	5.00	6.00	3.00
9	Sugar bowl		63	5.00	7.00	3.00
10	Sugar bowl, lid		95	9.00	12.00	6.00
11	Teapot, 4-cup		153	35.00	45.00	22.00

S
E
A
G
O
E

CLASSIC LINEN DESIGN

Produced by Wade Ireland with a short production run.

Backstamp: Blue printed semi-circular "Made In Ireland Wade Classic Linen
eire tir A dheanta" with two forget-me-not flowers

No.	Description	Colourways	Size	U.S. $	Can. $	U.K. £
1	Coffee cup and saucer	White; pale blue forget-me-nots/ linen panels	57/140	4.00	6.00	3.00
2	Coffee pot		229	30.00	40.00	20.00
3	Cream jug		95	4.00	6.00	3.00
4	Cup and saucer		63/149	4.00	6.00	3.00
5	Dinner plate		264	9.00	12.00	6.00
6	Gravy boat		82	6.00	8.00	4.00
7	Lunch plate		229	9.00	12.00	6.00
8	Pepper		80	5.00	6.00	3.00
9	Salt		80	5.00	6.00	3.00
10	Sugar bowl		63	5.00	7.00	3.00
11	Sugar bowl, lid		95	9.00	12.00	6.00
12	Teapot, 4-cup		153	34.00	44.00	22.00

S
E
A
G
O
E

MEADOWLAND DESIGN

Backstamp: Printed "Meadowland Dishwasher Safe Wade UK Fine Quality Tableware"

No.	Description	Colourways	Size	U.S. $	Can. $	U.K. £
1	Cream jug	White; blackberries; multi-coloured flowers	95	8.00	10.00	5.00
2	Cup and saucer		60/149	12.00	15.00	8.00
3	Dinner plate		264	10.00	12.00	6.00
4	Gravy boat		82	8.00	10.00	5.00
5	Lunch plate		229	10.00	12.00	6.00
6	Pepper		76	6.00	8.00	4.00
7	Salt		88	6.00	8.00	4.00
8	Sugar bowl		63	8.00	10.00	5.00
9	Sugar bowl, lid		95	10.00	12.00	6.00
10	Teapot, 4-cup		153	25.00	35.00	18.00

MUSIC DESIGN

Backstamp: Printed "Music a Peter Ting Design Exclusive to Wade UK Fine Tableware"

No.	Description	Colourways	Size	U.S. $	Can. $	U.K. £
1	Breakfast plate	White; black/white bars; multi-coloured notes	177	8.00	10.00	5.00
2	Coffee cup and saucer		57/140	4.00	6.00	3.00
3	Coffee pot		229	30.00	40.00	20.00
4	Cream jug		95	4.00	6.00	3.00
5	Cup and saucer		60/171	8.00	10.00	5.00
6	Dinner plate		264	10.00	12.00	6.00
7	Gravy boat		82	6.00	8.00	4.00
8	Lunch plate		229	10.00	12.00	6.00
9	Pepper		80	6.00	8.00	4.00
10	Salt		80	6.00	8.00	4.00
11	Sugar bowl		63	5.00	7.00	3.00
12	Sugar bowl, lid		95	10.00	12.00	6.00
13	Tea plate		159	8.00	10.00	5.00
14	Teapot, 4-cup		153	25.00	35.00	18.00

ROSE "CHINTZ" DESIGN

This set was available in both a pink and a blue colourway. See page 160 for the blue colourway.

Backstamp: Printed "Rose Chintz Wade UK Fine Quality Tableware"

No.	Description	Colourways	Size	U.S. $	Can. $	U.K. £
1	Coffee cup and saucer	White; pink flowers	57/140	8.00	10.00	5.00
2	Coffee pot		229	35.00	45.00	22.00
3	Cream jug		95	6.00	8.00	4.00
4	Cup and saucer		60/171	8.00	10.00	5.00
5	Gravy boat		82	6.00	8.00	4 .00
6	Lunch plate		229	9.00	12.00	6.00
7	Pepper		80	5.00	6.00	3.00
8	Salt		80	5.00	6.00	3.00
9	Sugar bowl		63	5.00	7.00	3.00
10	Sugar bowl, lid		95	9.00	12.00	6.00
11	Teapot, 4-cup		153	35.00	45.00	22.00

SPLASH DESIGN, 1988-1989

The teapot is in the Samantha shape and the cream and sugar are in the Victoria shape.

SEAGOE

Backstamp: Printed "Wade England"
Colourways: **A.** White; blue splashes
         B. White; multi-coloured splashes
         C. White; peach splashes

No.	Description	Size	U.S. $	Can. $	U.K. £
1	Cream jug	95	5.00	6.00	3.00
2	Milk jug	133	12.00	15.00	8.00
3	Pepper	108	3.00	4.00	2.00
4	Salt	108	3.00	4.00	2.00
5	Sugar bowl	76	4.00	5.00	2.00
6	Teapot	155	20.00	30.00	15.00
7	Toast rack	76	10.00	12.00	6.00

SUMMER FRUITS DESIGN

Backstamp: Printed "Summer Fruits Wade UK Fine Quality Tableware"

No.	Description	Colourways	Size	U.S. $	Can. $	U.K. £
1	Cream jug	White; multi-coloured fruits	95	8.00	10.00	5.00
2	Cup and saucer		60/171	8.00	10.00	5.00
3	Lunch plate		229	10.00	12.00	6.00
4	Pepper		80	6.00	8.00	4.00
5	Salt		80	6.00	8.00	4.00
6	Sugar bowl		63	5.00	7.00	3.00
7	Sugar bowl, lidded		95	10.00	12.00	6.00
8	Teapot		153	25.00	35.00	18.00

WALT DISNEY, 1938

BUNNIES AND FAWNS DESIGN

Egg Cups on Tray

Fruit Bowl

Backstamp: Ink stamp "Wadeheath by permission Walt Disney England"

No.	Description	Colourways	Size	U.S. $	Can. $	U.K. £
1	Egg cups/tray	Cups — cream; brown rabbit	63/120	200.00	275.00	100.00
		Tray — cream; green leaf design around the rim				
2	Fruit bowl	Cream; brown tree; green leaves;	45 x 229	200.00	270.00	135.00
		blue birds; brown fawns; yellow rabbits				
3	Toast rack	Cream; brown rabbits on each end	65 x 110	150.00	200.00	95.00

DONALD DUCK DESIGN

Backstamp: A. Black ink stamp "Wadeheath By Permission Walt Disney England"
B. Black ink stamp "Wadeheath England By Permission Walt Disney"

No.	Description	Colourways	Size	U.S. $	Can. $	U.K. £
1	Cream jug	Dark yellow	unknown	Very Rare		
2	Sugar bowl	Dark yellow	unknown	Very Rare		
3	Teapot, 4-cup	White; black eyes; dark yellow beak,hands, legs; blue hat, jacket; orange bow tie	160 x 220	800.00	900.00	450.00
4a	Teapot, 2-cup	White; black eyes; dark yellow beak, jacket, hands, feet; orange hat, bow tie	101 x 140	750.00	850.00	400.00
4b	Teapot, 2-cup	White; black eyes; bright yellow beak, hands, buttons, legs, pale blue hat, jacket; orange bow tie;	101 x 140	750.00	850.00	400.00
4c	Teapot, 2-cup	Dark yellow	101 x 140	650.00	800.00	350.00

SNOW WHITE DESIGN

Each item in this series has an embossed background design of bark and embossed multi-coloured Snow White figures. Happy and Sleepy are the pepper and salt sitting with their backs to a tree stump which is the mustard pot. The butter dish has a boxed base and the cheese dish has a flat base.

Biscuit Barrel

Butter Dish, Round

Butter Dish, Square

Cheese Dish, Cottage

Backstamp: Ink stamp "Wadeheath by permission Walt Disney England"

No.	Description	Colourways	Size	U.S. $	Can. $	U.K. £
1	Biscuit barrel (Snow White)	Cream; brown tree; green leaves; yellow dress; maroon bodice; brown rabbits; brown fox finial on lid	180	500.00	670.00	335.00
2a	Butter dish, round (Dopey)	Cream; brown tree; green leaves; brown rabbits; bluebirds; purple hat/trousers; orange coat; Dopey finial	115 x 170	225.00	300.00	150.00
2b	Butter dish, round (Dopey)	Blue	115 x 170	190.00	250.00	125.00
2c	Butter dish, round (Dopey)	Pink	115 x 170	190.00	250.00	125.00
3	Butter dish, square (Dopey)	Cream; brown tree; green leaves; brown rabbits; bluebirds; orange hat; maroon coat; blue trousers	100	190.00	250.00	125.00
4	Cheese dish (Cottage)	Yellow pointed roof; crooked brown fir tree; brown beams/windows/door; green base and tray edges	130 x 180	500.00	670.00	375.00

Cruet

Hot Water Jug

Milk Jug

Sugar Bowl

Teapot

W
A
L
T

D
I
S
N
E
Y

Backstamp: Ink stamp "Wadeheath by permission Walt Disney England"

No.	Description	Colourways	Size	U.S. $	Can. $	U.K. £
5	Cruet (Sleepy/Happy)	Mustard —Cream/green/brown tray, pot; blue bird finial; Pepper and Salt — maroon/ yellow/ brown	60 x 76	175.00	225.00	100.00
6	Honey/jam pot (Doc)	Cream; green leaves; purple/brown clothes; brown tree, rabbit, chipmunk finial	110	270.00	350.00	175.00
7	Hot water jug (Dopey)	Cream; brown tree; green leaves; purple/ maroon clothes; brown shoes; brown rabbit, fawn; blue bird; brown squirrel finial on lid	195	500.00	670.00	335.00
8	Milk jug (Sneezy)	Cream jug; brown tree; green leaves; purple/ maroon clothes; brown shoes; brown fox	93	220.00	300.00	150.00
9	Mustard pot/tray	Cream/green/brown tray, pot; blue bird finial	60 x 76	40.00	60.00	30.00
10	Pepper pot (Happy)	Yellow hat, trousers; maroon jacket; brown shoes	54	40.00	60.00	30.00
11	Salt pot (Sleepy)	Maroon jacket; yellow trousers; brown shoes	54	40.00	60.00	30.00
12	Sandwich platter oval (Dopey)	Cream/green; brown tree, shoes, squirrels; yellow hat; purple coat;	229	150.00	200.00	100.00
13	Sugar bowl (Bashful)	Cream; brown tree; green leaves; purple/maroon clothes; brown shoes; bluebirds; brown chipmunk finial	101	220.00	300.00	150.00
14	Teapot (Grumpy)	Cream; brown tree, shoes, fawn, squirrel finial; green leaves; maroon/purple clothes; blue bird	165	600.00	800.00	400.00

WHIRLOW HALL FARMHOUSE DESIGN BREAKFAST SET, 1995

The prints and quotes on this breakfast set (including the grammar and spelling mistakes) were taken from drawings made by Sheffield School children who visited Whirlow Hall farm. Mugs were made in both Earthenware (Version 1) and Porcelain (Version 2) with the same designs used on both.

Item	Edition Size	Designs
Bowls	1,308	2
Egg cups	4,140	2
Mugs, Version 1	1,503	4
Mugs, Version 2	1,260	4
Plates	Unknown	2
Teapots	250	2

W H I R L O W   H A L L

Mug, 2c; Mug, 2b

Mug, 2a; Mug, 2d

Backstamp: Black printed "Whirlow Hall Farmhouse Wade English Fine Bone China Designed by Sheffield Children" with or without child's name and age

No.	Description	Colourways	Size	U.S. $	Can. $	U.K. £
1a	Bowl	White; multi-coloured print of a duck; "A Duck has got long feat"	168	12.00	15.00	8.00
2a	Mug, Ver. 1		95	5.00	6.00	3.00
3a	Mug, Ver. 2		110	8.00	10.00	4.00
4a	Plate		192	12.00	15.00	8.00
5a	Teapot		unknown	22.00	30.00	15.00
1b	Bowl	White; multi-coloured print of a scarecrow; "I like the muddy fields"	168	12.00	15.00	8.00
2b	Mug, Ver. 1		95	5.00	6.00	3.00
3b	Mug, Ver. 2		110	8.00	10.00	4.00
4b	Plate		192	12.00	15.00	8.00
5b	Teapot		unknown	22.00	30.00	15.00
2c	Mug, Ver. 1	White; multi-coloured print of a chick; "Howards Feathers are nice and soft"	95	5.00	6.00	3.00
3c	Mug, Ver. 2		110	8.00	10.00	4.00
2d	Mug, Ver. 1	White; multi-coloured print of a rabbit; "We was giving the rabbit sum dandilion"	95	5.00	6.00	3.00
3d	Mug, Ver. 2		110	8.00	10.00	4.00
6a	Egg cup	White; multi-coloured print of ears of corn	50	4.00	6.00	3.00
6b	Egg cup	White; multi-coloured print of a flower	50	4.00	6.00	3.00

TEAPOTS AND COFFEE POTS

John Wade's Teapots
Teapots
Novelty Teapots
Stands for Teapots
Coffee Items and Sets

Excelsior Shapes

John Wade's Teapots and Accompaniments c.1880s-1902

These beautiful ornately shaped and hand-decorated teapots and their accompaniments are the earliest known "Wade" products. The accompaniments could be a kettle, a teapot stand, a hot water jug, a milk jug, a cream jug or a sugar bowl. Hot water jugs had a pewter rimmed lid which has a white bead knob to raise the lid. The lid and rim was attached to a pivot fitted into two holes on the rim of the jug, constant use often broke the metal pivot hinge and the pewter rim and lid was then discarded. Jugs that have lost their lids can be distinguished from the milk jugs by the two holes in the rim that originally held the lid in place.

The method of decoration is unusual, the shape of the flowers and leaves have been "etched" off the green panels exposing the black glaze underneath, the exposed design is then filled in with the colours and gold leaf hence the rough edge appearance to some of the gold striped leaves.

The white or gold ink backstamp is a ribbon wreath within which is the design name and W & Co B. Underneath the wreath is a gold handwritten or stamped registration number and a handwritten pattern number, the decorator's initial is sometimes included. As with all ink stamps, constant use and washing wear away the marks and sometimes only a few faint traces of gold numbers remain.

There are three clay pad marks in a triangle on the base. The clay pads held the piece steady during its journey through the kiln, once it reached the end the pads were broken off which left three small bubble like pads often with a white centre.

SHAPE NAME INDEX

ACME SHAPE, c.1899

GARLAND DESIGN

Backstamp: Ink stamp white circular ribbon wreath "Acme W & Co B" gold REGd 343857 "2096" (pattern No)

No.	Description	Colourways	Size	U.S. $	Can. $	U.K. £
1	Hot water jug	Black; grey/green panels; green garland; green/ white/pink forget-me-not flowers; green leaves	185	185.00	300.00	150.00

IVY LEAF DESIGN

Backstamp: Ink stamp white circular ribbon wreath "Acme W & Co B" gold REGd 343857 "2096" (pattern No)

No.	Description	Colourways	Size	U.S. $	Can. $	U.K. £
1	Hot water jug	Black; grey/green panels; pink forget-me-not flowers; black/gold ivy leaves, herring bone stripes	185	135.00	175.00	90.00

A
C
M
E

BRITANNIA SHAPE, c.1901

The teapot gets its name from the shape of the lid finial which resembles the helmet worn by the British figure "Britannia."

BERRIES AND FLOWERS DESIGN

Backstamp: Ink stamp white circular ribbon wreath "Britannia W & Co B" gold: REGd 369349 "1 /1" (pattern No)

No.	Description	Colourways	Size	U.S. $	Can. $	U.K. £
1	Teapot	Black; grey/green panels; orange berries; gold/white flowers	162	270.00	370.00	185.00

CENTURY SHAPE, c.1888

GARLAND DESIGN

Backstamp: Ink stamp white circular ribbon wreath "Century W & Co B"

No.	Description	Colourways	Size	U.S. $	Can. $	U.K. £
1	Hot water jug	Black; grey/green panel; green garland; white/pink forget-me-not flowers; green leaves	180	185.00	300.00	150.00
2	Teapot	Black; grey/green panel; green garland; white/pink forget-me-not flowers; green leaves	165	270.00	370.00	185.00

WILD VIOLETS DESIGN

Backstamp: Ink stamp white circular ribbon wreath "Century W & Co B"

No.	Description	Colourways	Size	U.S. $	Can. $	U.K. £
1	Teapot	Cream/gold; violet flowers; pale green leaves	200	250.00	350.00	250.00

EUREKA SHAPE, c.1895

FERN AND BERRIES DESIGN

Backstamp: A. Ink stamp gold circular ribbon wreath "Eureka W & Co B" Gold regd No "Rd 282788"
B. Ink stamp gold circular ribbon wreath "Eureka W & Co B" Gold regd No "Rd 282788"
"V816" (pattern No)

No.	Description	Colourways	Size	U.S. $	Can. $	U.K. £
1	Hot water jug	Black; grey/green panel; gold fern leaves; white berries	184	185.00	300.00	150.00
2	Teapot		159	270.00	370.00	185.00

FORGET-ME-NOTS DESIGN

Backstamp: A. Ink stamp gold circular ribbon wreath "Eureka W & Co B" Gold regd No "Rd 282788"
B. Ink stamp gold circular ribbon wreath "Eureka W & Co B" Gold regd No "Rd 282788"
"V816" (pattern No)

No.	Description	Colourways	Size	U.S. $	Can. $	U.K. £
1	Hot water jug	Black; grey/green panel; white forget-me-not flowers; gold leaves	184	185.00	300.00	150.00

EXCELSIOR SHAPE, c.1894

FORGET-ME-NOTS DESIGN

Backstamp: **A.** Ink stamp gold circular ribbon wreath "Excelsior W & Co B" Gold Regd No "REGd 220194" "e 544" (pattern no.)
B. Gold ink stamp circular ribbon wreath "Excelsior W & Co B" Gold Regd No "REGd 220194 '763'" (pattern no.)
C. Gold ink stamp "Patent locks lid prevents overflow. Regd No '220194' '763'" (pattern no.)

No.	Description	Colourways	Size	U.S. $	Can. $	U.K. £
1a	Hot water jug	Black; grey/green panels; blue forget-me-not flowers; white berries	168	185.00	300.00	150.00
1b	Hot water jug	Black; grey/green panels; blue forget-me-not flowers; white dots; gold ribbon	168	185.00	300.00	150.00
2	Lock lid teapot		146	270.00	370.00	185.00

IVY LEAVES DESIGN

Backstamp: None

No.	Description	Colourways	Size	U.S. $	Can. $	U.K. £
1	Hot water jug	Black; green ivy leaves with gold veins; white berries; small gold leaves	168	185.00	300.00	150.00

LEAVES AND BERRIES DESIGN

This unusual teapot is equipped with an infuser, patented by William Wade.

Backstamp: Gold ink stamp "Patent locks lid prevents overflow. Gold Regd No REGd 220194"

No.	Description	Colourways	Size	U.S. $	Can. $	U.K. £
1	Teapot (with infuser)	Black; green panel; gold leaves; white berries	146	270.00	370.00	185.00

LILY OF THE VALLEY DESIGN

The Lily of the Valley teapot has a "locks lid" and is a shape that is known to have been adapted for the new "hook and locks lid."

Backstamp: Gold ink stamp "Patent locks lid prevents overflow. Gold Regd No REGd 220194"

No.	Description	Colourways	Size	U.S. $	Can. $	U.K. £
1	Lock lid teapot	Black; grey/green panels; gold and white lily of the valley flowers, leaves	146	270.00	370.00	185.00

SHAMROCK AND FERN LEAVES DESIGN

Backstamp: None

No.	Description	Colourways	Size	U.S. $	Can. $	U.K. £
1	Stand for teapot	Black; green panel; black shamrocks; blue fern leaves; small white flowers	205	70.00	90.00	45.00

EXCELSIOR

GADROON SHAPE, c.1900

GARLAND DESIGN

Backstamp: Ink stamp gold circular ribbon wreath "Gadroon W & Co B" Gold Regd No "Rd 355036"

No.	Description	Colourways	Size	U.S. $	Can. $	U.K. £
1	Teapot	Black; grey/green panels; light green garland; pink, green, white forget-me-not flowers	171	270.00	370.00	185.00

Note: The teapot illustrated above is shown with an incorrect lid. Reference is for pattern only.

IVY DESIGN

Backstamp: Ink stamp gold circular ribbon wreath "Gadroon W & Co B" Gold Regd No "Rd 355036"

No.	Description	Colourways	Size	U.S. $	Can. $	U.K. £
1	Teapot	Black; grey/green panels; blue forget-me-not flowers; black/gold ivy leaves	171	270.00	370.00	185.00

GLADSTONE SHAPE, 1899

FORGET-ME-NOTS DESIGN

Backstamp: Ink stamp gold circular ribbon wreath "W & Co B Gladstone' gold reg No. 315844' "

No.	Description	Colourways	Size	U.S. $	Can. $	U.K. £
1	Chocolate pot	Black; green panels; blue forget-me-not flowers; orange berries; gold highlighting	159	270.00	370.00	185.00

GOLD DAISIES DESIGN

Backstamp: Ink stamp gold circular ribbon wreath "W & Co B Gladstone"

No.	Description	Colourways	Size	U.S. $	Can. $	U.K. £
1	Hot water jug	Black; grey/green bands; gold daisy type flowers with turquoise centres, gold leaves; turquoise dots	177	185.00	300.00	150.00

I
M
P
E
R
I
A
L

IMPERIAL SHAPE, 1902

Backstamp: Ink stamp gold circular ribbon wreath "Imperial W & Co B" gold regd No "Rd 3656-1" "3038"(pattern No)

No.	Description	Colourways	Size	U.S. $	Can. $	U.K. £
1	Sugar bowl	Black; grey/green panels; small white berries; blue forget-me-not flowers; black ivy leaves	115	125.00	190.00	95.00

MAFEKING SHAPE, 1900

Backstamp: Ink stamp gold circular ribbon wreath "Mafeking W & Co B" Gold Regd No "Rd 382006

No.	Description	Colourways	Size	U.S. $	Can. $	U.K. £
1	Teapot	Black; black and gold ivy leaves; grey/green body; pink forget-me-not flowers; white berries	140	270.00	370.00	185.00

QUEEN SHAPE, c.1890

IVY DESIGN

Backstamp: Gold "I.P.S."

No.	Description	Colourways	Size	U.S. $	Can. $	U.K. £
1	Hot water jug	Black; green ivy leaves with yellow veins; gold highlighting	165	250.00	300.00	150.00

WHITE FORGET-ME-NOTS DESIGN

Backstamp: Unmarked

No.	Description	Colourways	Size	U.S. $	Can. $	U.K. £
1	Hot water jug	Black; white flowers; gold leaves and highlighting	171	120.00	160.00	80.00
2	Milk jug		76	65.00	90.00	45.00
3	Stand for teapot		159	50.00	65.00	35.00
4	Sugar bowl		88	65.00	90.00	45.00
5	Teapot		153	135.00	180.00	90.00

QUEEN

REGINA SHAPE, c.1897

This teapot was produced to celebrate the Diamond Jubilee of Queen Victoria in 1897.

FORGET-ME-NOTS AND BERRIES DESIGN

Backstamp: Unmarked

No.	Description	Colourways	Size	U.S. $	Can. $	U.K. £
1	Teapot	Black; grey/green panels; blue dots; gold striped leaves; small white flowers	165	325.00	430.00	225.00

UNKNOWN SHAPES, c. 1888-1902

Since the shape names for these pieces are unknown, we have listed them alphabetically by design name.

APPLE BLOSSOM DESIGN

Backstamp: Gold "ca 7" or "ba 7"

No.	Description	Colourways	Size	U.S. $	Can. $	U.K. £
1	Hot water jug	Black; grey/green panels; white blossoms; orange dots; turquoise dots; gold striped leaves	168	185.00	300.00	150.00

BLOSSOM DESIGN

Backstamp: Unmarked

No.	Description	Colourways	Size	U.S. $	Can. $	U.K. £
1	Teapot	Black; grey/green panel; pinky white blossoms; gold veined leaves; white dots	153	145.00	160.00	85.00

CORNFLOWER DESIGN, c.1890

Backstamp: Unmarked

No.	Description	Colourways	Size	U.S. $	Can. $	U.K. £
1	Kettle	Black; grey/green panels; blue cornflowers, dots; small pink/white flowers; gold leaves, highlights	195	270.00	370.00	185.00

DAFFODILS DESIGN, c.1888

This is a lock lid teapot.

Backstamp: Unmarked

No.	Description	Colourways	Size	U.S. $	Can. $	U.K. £
1	Teapot	Black; grey/green panel; gold daffodil flowers, leaves	146	270.00	370.00	185.00

DAISY AND FORGET-ME-NOT DESIGN

Backstamp: Unmarked

No.	Description	Colourways	Size	U.S. $	Can. $	U.K. £
1	Teapot	Black; green panel; dull yellow forget-me-not flowers; black gold veined leaves; white daisies with yellow centres; gold highlights	170	225.00	350.00	175.00

FAN DESIGN

Backstamp: Gold "455" or "655"

No.	Description	Colourways	Size	U.S. $	Can. $	U.K. £
1	Stand for teapot	Black; grey blue green panels; gold fan/leaves/flowers	205	125.00	190.00	95.00
2	Teapot		155	270.00	370.00	185.00

FORGET-ME-NOTS DESIGN

Backstamp: Unknown

No.	Description	Colourways	Size	U.S. $	Can. $	U.K. £
1	Hot water jug	Black; grey/green panels; blue forget-me-not flowers; white berries	210	185.00	300.00	150.00

GOLD LEAVES DESIGN

Backstamp: Gold "936h"

No.	Description	Colourways	Size	U.S. $	Can. $	U.K. £
1	Hot water jug	Black; grey/green panels; gold leaves and flowers	160	185.00	300.00	150.00

GOLD LEAVES AND FLOWERS DESIGN, c.1888

This teapot has the patented "hook lid."

Backstamp: Unknown

No.	Description	Colourways	Size	U.S. $	Can. $	U.K. £
1	Teapot	Black; grey/green panels; gold leaves/flowers	165	270.00	370.00	185.00

GOLD LOOPS DESIGN

Although this teapot does not have the grey-blue green panels of all the other John Wade items listed, it does have the gold loop design seen on the Daffodil teapot and the Fan teapot.

Backstamp: Unknown

No.	Description	Colourways	Size	U.S. $	Can. $	U.K. £
1	Teapot	Black; gold loops/scallop shells	145	170.00	230.00	115.00

IVY LEAVES DESIGN

Style One

The lid on this teapot is referred to as an "automatic lock lid."

Backstamp: Embossed "Wade Patent" on underside of lid, gold handwritten "369" on base

No.	Description	Colourways	Size	U.S. $	Can. $	U.K. £
1	Hot water jug	Black; green ivy leaves with yellow veins; gold highlighting	184	185.00	300.00	150.00
2	Teapot		153	270.00	370.00	185.00

Style 2

The ivy leaf pattern found on this round-footed teapot is similar to that found on the Excelsior teapot and hot water jug (see page 183).

Backstamp: None

No.	Description	Colourways	Size	U.S. $	Can. $	U.K. £
1	Teapot	Black; large green ivy leaves with gold veins; small gold leaves	175	240.00	300.00	150.00

Style 3

The ivy leaf pattern on these square-footed teapots varies from the large to small size, with the smaller size having more gold highlights.

Backstamp: Unmarked

No.	Description	Colourways	Size	U.S. $	Can. $	U.K. £
1	Teapot, 6-cup	Black; large green ivy leaves with gold veins; small gold leaves	170	240.00	300.00	150.00
2	Teapot, 4-cup		145	240.00	300.00	150.00

LEAVES AND BERRIES DESIGN, c.1899

While the pattern on these three pieces is the same, the teapot handle is a different shape than the cream jug.

Backstamp: Gold with registration mark

No.	Description	Colourways	Size	U.S. $	Can. $	U.K. £
1	Cream jug	Black; grey-green panels; gold leaves; orange/white berries	87	60.00	100.00	50.00
2	Sugar bowl		50	55.00	80.00	40.00
3	Teapot		170	270.00	370.00	185.00

SNOWDROPS DESIGN

UNKNOWN

Backstamp: Gold "978 II"

No.	Description	Colourways	Size	U.S. $	Can. $	U.K. £
1	Teapot	Black; grey/green panels; white snowdrops and beaded garlands; gold leaves; orange berries	160	270.00	370.00	185.00

Teapots

The teapots listed in this section are those that were produced as either a single teapot with no matching items, or a teapot with only one or two matching items and are thus not considered sets.

SHAPE NAME INDEX

BEE SHAPE, 1932-c.1940

FLORAL CHINTZ DESIGN

This octagonal shaped teapot was first advertised in 1932.

Backstamp: Black ink stamp "Wade Heath England J" (1939-c.1948)

No.	Description	Colourways	Size	U.S. $	Can. $	U.K. £
1	Teapot, 6-cup	White; blue/pink flowers; grey leaves	159	165.00	200.00	100.00

FLORAL FENCE DESIGN

Photograph of design
not available
at press time

Backstamp: Black ink stamp "Wadeheath England" with lion (1934-37)

No.	Description	Colourways	Size	U.S. $	Can. $	U.K. £
1	Teapot, 6-cup	Cream; yellow/orange flowers; green leaves; brown fence	159	75.00	100.00	50.00

FLOWERS AND SCROLL DESIGN

Backstamp: Orange ink stamp "Wades England" with lion (1927-1933)

No.	Description	Colourways	Size	U.S. $	Can. $	U.K. £
1	Teapot, 6-cup	White; bright yellow/dark blue scroll; orange flowers; dark blue/green leaves	159	75.00	100.00	50.00

FUSCHIA DESIGN

Backstamp: Black ink stamp "Wadeheath England" with lion (1934-1937)

No.	Description	Colourways	Size	U.S. $	Can. $	U.K. £
1	Teapot, 6-cup	Cream; bright yellow/orange and yellow/violet flowers; green leaves	159	75.00	100.00	50.00

PAISLEY DESIGN

For an illustration
of this design
see page 29

Backstamp: Black ink stamp "Wade Heath England" (1939-c.1948)

No.	Description	Colourways	Size	U.S. $	Can. $	U.K. £
1	Teapot, 6-cup	White/multi-coloured print	159	175.00	200.00	100.00

BUTE SHAPE, c.1933

This round two-tone teapot is similar in shape to the popular Nelson teapots, but Bute has a row of embossed dots around the middle and a shorter spout.

Backstamp: Red ink stamp "Wades England" with lion "H 1829" (c.1927-1933)

No.	Description	Colourways	Size	U.S. $	Can. $	U.K. £
1	Teapot, 6-cup	Honey yellow lid, base; black spout, band and handle; pink flowers; gold highlights	159	100.00	130.00	65.00

CANTON SHAPE, 1931 - c.1945

This decagonal (ten sided) shaped teapot is similar to the Clifton shape (see page 26). The first advertisement of this shape is in 1931.

FLOWERS AND GOLD LEAVES DESIGN

Backstamp: Ink stamp "Wade Heath England" (straight W c.1945-c.1952)

No.	Description	Colourways	Size	U.S. $	Can. $	U.K. £
1	Teapot, 6-cup	Black; orange/pale blue flowers; gold leaves and highlighting	159	50.00	65.00	30.00

FLOWERS AND GOLD SWIRLS DESIGN

Backstamp: Ink stamp "Wadeheath England" with lion (1933-1394)

No.	Description	Colourways	Size	U.S. $	Can. $	U.K. £
1	Teapot, 6-cup	Black; orange flowers; white spots; gold swirls	159	50.00	65.00	30.00

WHITE WITH MULTI-COLOURED FLOWERS DESIGN

Photograph of this design not available at press time

Backstamp: Orange-red ink stamp "Wades England" with lion (1927-1933)

No.	Description	Colourways	Size	U.S. $	Can. $	U.K. £
1	Teapot, 6-cup	White; multi-coloured flowers	159	50.00	65.00	30.00

EAGLE HANDLE SHAPE, c.1940 - 1953

The teapot is easy to identify by the moulded eagle with open wings which forms the handle, they are found with all over copper lustre, copper lustre with hand painted decoration, or copper lustre with a wide coloured band (usually cream) which was hand-decorated with flowers and leaves.

ASTER DESIGN

Backstamp: Ink stamp "Harvest Ware Wade England" (c.1948-1953)

No.	Description	Colourways	Size	U.S. $	Can. $	U.K. £
1a	Teapot, 6-cup	Copper lustre; yellow/green leaves; large pink aster flowers	150	110.00	150.00	75.00
1b	Teapot, 6-cup	Cream; yellow/green leaves; large pink aster flowers	150	110.00	150.00	75.00

COPPER LUSTRE DESIGN

Photograph of this
design not available
at press time

Backstamp: Ink stamp "Harvest Ware Wade England" (c.1948-1953)

No.	Description	Colourways	Size	U.S. $	Can. $	U.K. £
1	Teapot, 6-cup	Copper lustre	150	60.00	80.00	45.00

GREEN BAND DESIGN

Photograph of this
design not available
at press time

Backstamp: Black ink stamp "Wade England" (c.1948-1953)

No.	Description	Colourways	Size	U.S. $	Can. $	U.K. £
1	Teapot, 6-cup	Copper lustre; pale green band; green fern leaves; small pink flowers	150	110.00	150.00	75.00

LEAVES DESIGN

Photograph of this
design not available
at press time

Backstamp: Ink stamp "Harvest Ware Wade England" (c.1948-1953)

No.	Description	Colourways	Size	U.S. $	Can. $	U.K. £
1	Teapot, 6-cup	Copper; cream band; large grey leaves	150	110.00	150.00	75.00

PHLOX DESIGN

Backstamp: Ink stamp "Harvest Ware Wade England" (c.1948-1953)

No.	Description	Colourways	Size	U.S. $	Can. $	U.K. £
1	Teapot, 6-cup	Copper lustre; cream band; green leaves; small pink flowers	150	110.00	150.00	75.00

VINE AND BERRIES DESIGN

For an illustration
of this design
see page 43

Backstamp: Ink stamp "Harvest Ware Wade England" (c.1948-1953)

No.	Description	Colourways	Size	U.S. $	Can. $	U.K. £
1	Teapot, 6-cup	Copper lustre rim/handle/base; blue band; copper vine, leaves, berries	150	110.00	150.00	75.00

FORTH SHAPE, c.1932

The Forth shape teapot is very similar in shape to the Selby (see page 224), but does not have the two embossed bands of dots around the neck.

GOLD BAND DESIGN

Photograph of this
design not available
at press time

Backstamp: Orange ink stamp "Wades England" with lion (1927-1933)

No.	Description	Colourways	Size	U.S. $	Can. $	U.K. £
1	Teapot, 4-cup	Black; gold band; grey black flowers and scroll	140	70.00	90.00	45.00

PAISLEY DESIGN

Backstamp: Black ink stamp "Wade Heath England A" (1939-1945)

No.	Description	Colourways	Size	U.S. $	Can. $	U.K. £
1	Teapot, 6-cup	Paisley chintz	153	175.00	200.00	100.00

Note: This teapot is shown with an incorrect lid.

JUPITER SHAPE, 1931

Jupiter teapots are similar in shape to the popular Nelson teapots (see page 210). The lid sits inside the neck and the finial is round. The first advertisement date is 1931.

CRAZY PAVING DESIGN

Photograph of this
design not available
at press time

Backstamp: Orange ink stamp "Wades England" with lion

No.	Description	Colourways	Size	U.S. $	Can. $	U.K. £
1	Teapot, 3-cup	Black lid/bottom; grey/brown crazy paving	127	40.00	50.00	25.00

STRIPED BOX AND FLOWER DESIGN

Photograph of this
design not available
at press time

Backstamp: Orange ink stamp "Wades England" with lion

No.	Description	Colourways	Size	U.S. $	Can. $	U.K. £
1	Teapot, 3-cup	Brown lid/bottom; cream banded top with black striped box and blue flower	127	40.00	50.00	25.00

YELLOW FLOWER DESIGN

Photograph of this
design not available
at press time

Backstamp: Orange ink stamp "Wades England" with lion

No.	Description	Colourways	Size	U.S. $	Can. $	U.K. £
1	Teapot, 3-cup	Black lid/bottom; cream banded top with small yellow flowers	127	40.00	50.00	25.00

KETTLE SHAPE, 1927-1933

This ornate teapot is shaped as a kettle and has a large looping handle above the pot.

PAISLEY DESIGN

For an illustration
of this design
see page 29

Backstamp: Orange ink stamp "Wades England" with lion

No.	Description	Colourways	Size	U.S. $	Can. $	U.K. £
1	Teapot, 6-cup	Paisley chintz	159	175.00	200.00	100.00

KEW SHAPE, 1931-1933

1931 is the earliest found advertisement date for this unusual shaped teapot which has inward curving sides and a short spout, the finial on the lid is triangular with two holes through it.

DAISY CHAIN DESIGN

Photograph of this
design not available
at press time

Backstamp: Orange ink stamp "Wades England" with lion (1927-1933)

No.	Description	Colourways	Size	U.S. $	Can. $	U.K. £
1	Teapot, 4-cup	White pot; pink daisies; green chain; gold highlighting	140	100.00	135.00	65.00

PEACOCK DESIGN

Photograph of this
design not available
at press time

Backstamp: Orange ink stamp "Wades England" with lion (1927-1933)

No.	Description	Colourways	Size	U.S. $	Can. $	U.K. £
1	Teapot, 4-cup	Cream pot; multi-coloured peacock on floral tree branch	140	100.00	135.00	65.00

KETTLE

NELSON SHAPE, 1933-c.1962

The earliest advertisement found for the Nelson teapot is 1933. These teapots are almost identical to the Jupiter teapots being ball shaped with a round handle that has an embossed leaf thumb rest. Dandy jugs and sugar bowls were used to make three-piece sets with Nelson and other teapots (see cream jugs and sugar bowls section).

ASTER DESIGN

Backstamp: **A.** Black ink stamp "Wade England" (c.1948-1953)
B. Gold printed semi-circular "Wade made in England Hand Painted"

No.	Description	Colourways	Size	U.S. $	Can. $	U.K. £
1	Teapot, 4-cup	Copper lustre; pink flowers; yellow/green leaves	140	90.00	120.00	60.00
2	Teapot, 3-cup	Copper lustre; pink/mauve flowers; yellow/green leaves	127	60.00	80.00	40.00

COPPER DESIGN

Backstamp: Ink stamp "Harvest Ware Wade England" (c.1948-1953)

No.	Description	Colourways	Size	U.S. $	Can. $	U.K. £
1	Teapot, 3-cup	Copper lustre	127	60.00	80.00	40.00

COTONEASTER BERRIES DESIGN

For an illustration
of this design
see page 319

Backstamp: Ink stamp "Harvest Ware Wade England" (c.1948-1953)

No.	Description	Colourways	Size	U.S. $	Can. $	U.K. £
1	Teapot, 4-cup	Copper; yellow cotoneaster berries; pale green leaves	140	90.00	120.00	60.00

CRANBERRY DESIGN

This design has pointed leaves and berries

Photograph of this
design not available
at press time

Backstamp: Black ink stamp "Wade England" (c.1948-1953)

No.	Description	Colourways	Size	U.S. $	Can. $	U.K. £
1	Teapot, 4-cup	Copper top/base/spout/handle; cream band; red berries; green leaves	140	90.00	120.00	60.00

CROCUS DESIGN

Photograph of this
design not available
at press time

Backstamp: Black ink stamp "Wade England" (c.1948-1953)

No.	Description	Colourways	Size	U.S. $	Can. $	U.K. £
1	Teapot, 4-cup	Copper lustre; yellow/green leaves; large pink/yellow crocus flowers	140	90.00	120.00	60.00

DAISIES DESIGN

Variation 1 — Pointed petals

Backstamp: Black ink stamp "Wade England" (c.1948-1953)

No.	Description	Colourways	Size	U.S. $	Can. $	U.K. £
1	Teapot, 4-cup	Cream; maroon/purple flowers; green/brown leaves	140	90.00	120.00	60.00

Variation 2 — Round petals

For an illustration
of this design
see page 312

Backstamp: Black ink stamp "Wade England" (c.1948-1953)

No.	Description	Colourways	Size	U.S. $	Can. $	U.K. £
1	Teapot, 4-cup	Copper; cream band; maroon/purple flowers; green/brown leaves	140	90.00	120.00	60.00

FRUIT DESIGN

Photograph of this
design not available
at press time

Backstamp: Black ink stamp "Wade England" (c.1948-1953)

No.	Description	Colourways	Size	U.S. $	Can. $	U.K. £
1	Teapot, 2-cup	Cream; orange/yellow fruits; green leaves	114	70.00	90.00	45.00

GEORGIAN DESIGN

Backstamp: Black ink stamp "Wade Heath England A" (1939-1945)

No.	Description	Colourways	Size	U.S. $	Can. $	U.K. £
1	Teapot, 2-cup	White; copper neck, handle, base, flower heads, leaves	114	60.00	80.00	40.00

GEORGIAN OAK DESIGN

Backstamp: **A.** Black ink stamp "Wade Heath England"
                B. Black ink stamp "Wade Heath England A" (1939-1945)

No.	Description	Colourways	Size	U.S. $	Can. $	U.K. £
1	Teapot, 4-cup	Copper lustre; white leaves/acorns	140	90.00	120.00	60.00
2	Teapot, 3-cup		127	60.00	80.00	40.00

PEONY DESIGN

See page 302 for an illustration of this design

Backstamp: Ink stamp "Harvest Ware Wade England" (c.1948-1953)

No.	Description	Colourways	Size	U.S. $	Can. $	U.K. £
1	Teapot, 4-cup	Cream; copper lid/spout/handle/rims; large maroon flowers; copper leaves	140	90.00	120.00	60.00
2	Teapot, 3-cup		127	60.00	80.00	40.00

NELSON

PHLOX DESIGN

Dandy sugar bowl;   Nelson teapot;   Dandy cream jug

Backstamp: Gold printed semi-circular "Wade made in England Hand Painted"

No.	Description	Colourways	Size	U.S. $	Can. $	U.K. £
1	Teapot, 2-cup	Cream; copper lid/spout/handle/rims; large yellow/green leaves; small pink heart shaped flowers	114	60.00	80.00	40.00

PLUMS DESIGN

Backstamp: Gold printed semi-circular "Wade made in England Hand Painted"

No.	Description	Colourways	Size	U.S. $	Can. $	U.K. £
1	Teapot, 3-cup	Cream; copper lid/spout/handle/rims; large maroon/purple plums; green leaves	127	60.00	80.00	40.00

NELSON

POPPY DESIGN

Backstamp: A. Black ink stamp "Wade Heath England A" (1939-1945)
 B. Ink stamp "Harvest Ware Wade England" (c.1948-1953)

No.	Description	Colourways	Size	U.S. $	Can. $	U.K. £
1	Teapot, 4-cup	Cream; maroon/purple flowers/pod; green/brown leaves	140	90.00	120.00	60.00
2	Teapot, 3-cup	Cream; copper lid/spout/handle/rims; large maroon/purple flowers/pod; green leaves	127	60.00	80.00	40.00

SHAMROCK DESIGN

Backstamp: Black ink stamp "Wade England" (c.1948-1953)

No.	Description	Colourways	Size	U.S. $	Can. $	U.K. £
1	Teapot, 4-cup	Copper top/base/spout/handle; cream band; green shamrock leaves and stems	140	90.00	120.00	60.00

PEKIN SHAPE, 1930

The first advertisement found in the *Pottery and Glass Trades Review* for the Pekin shape teapot was January, 1930. It is advertised as "Wades Famous teapots finest ever Pekin No 6299 in rockingham (dark brown) samian, russet (red brown) mosaic, jet, solid green and white and designs."

CHERRY BLOSSOM DESIGN

Photograph of this
design not available
at press time

Backstamp: Orange ink stamp "Wades England" with lion (1927-1933)

No.	Description	Colourways	Size	U.S. $	Can. $	U.K. £
1	Teapot, 6-cup	Pale blue; pink/white blossoms	159	125.00	160.00	80.00

DAISY DESIGN

Backstamp: Orange ink stamp "Wades England" with lion (1927-1933)

No.	Description	Colourways	Size	U.S. $	Can. $	U.K. £
1	Teapot, 4-cup	Pale blue; pink flowers; gold highlights	135	60.00	90.00	45.00

P
E
K
I
N

FLORAL DESIGN

Backstamp: Orange ink stamp "Wades England" with lion Gold pattern No 6385 (1927-1933)

No.	Description	Colourways	Size	U.S. $	Can. $	U.K. £
1	Teapot, 4-cup	White; blue decorated band; orange flowers; blue leaves; gold/dark blue leaves	135	90.00	120.00	60.00

FLOWERS DESIGN

Photograph of this
design not available
at press time

Backstamp: Orange ink stamp "Wades England" with lion (1927-1933)

No.	Description	Colourways	Size	U.S. $	Can. $	U.K. £
1	Teapot, 6-cup	Black; gold neck; small red flowers	159	60.00	90.00	45.00

GOLD FLOWERS DESIGN

Photograph of this
design not available
at press time

Backstamp: Orange ink stamp "Wades England" with lion

No.	Description	Colourways	Size	U.S. $	Can. $	U.K. £
1	Teapot, 4-cup	Light blue; gold/ blue flowers	135	60.00	90.00	45.00

P
E
K
I
N

PLUM BLOSSOM DESIGN

Backstamp: Orange ink stamp "Wades England" with lion (1927-1933) (Gold pattern No 6151)

No.	Description	Colourways	Size	U.S. $	Can. $	U.K. £
1	Teapot, 6-cup	Dark blue;white blossoms; brown branches	159	125.00	160.00	80.00

SOLID COLOURS DESIGN

Photograph of this
design not available
at press time

Backstamp: Orange ink stamp "Wades England" with lion (1927-1933)

No.	Description	Colourways	Size	U.S. $	Can. $	U.K. £
1a	Teapot, 6-cup	Green	159	40.00	55.00	30.00
1b	Teapot, 6-cup	White	159	40.00	55.00	30.00

STRIPED DESIGN

Photograph of this
design not available
at press time

Backstamp: Orange ink stamp "Wades England" with lion (1927-1933)

No.	Description	Colourways	Size	U.S. $	Can. $	U.K. £
1	Teapot, 6-cup	White; blue band; white stripes; pink flowers	159	65.00	90.00	45.00

REGENCY ANNIVERSARY SHAPE, 1993

These ten-sided (decagonal) teapots were produced in the four colours representing the traditional wedding anniversaries of silver (25 years), pearl (30 years), ruby (40 years) and gold (50 years).

Backstamp: Printed "Wade England" with two lines

No.	Description	Colourways	Size	U.S. $	Can. $	U.K. £
1a	Teapot, 4-cup	Gold	140	45.00	60.00	30.00
1b	Teapot, 4-cup	Maroon; gold highlights	140	45.00	60.00	30.00
1c	Teapot, 4-cup	Pearlised; gold highlights	140	45.00	60.00	30.00
1d	Teapot, 4-cup	Silver	140	45.00	60.00	30.00

REGENCY COLLECTION SHAPE, 1993

STYLE 1   DOME LID; POINTED HEART-SHAPED HANDLE

FLORAL DESIGN

Photograph of this
design not available
at press time

Backstamp: Printed "The Regency Collection Made in Fine Bone China by Wade England"

No.	Description	Colourways	Size	U.S. $	Can. $	U.K. £
1	Teapot, 1-cup	White; small pink/blue flowers; gold highlighting	100	25.00	35.00	18.00

POT POURRI DESIGN

Backstamp: Printed "The Regency Collection Made in Fine Bone China by Wade England"

No.	Description	Colourways	Size	U.S. $	Can. $	U.K. £
1	Teapot, 1-cup	White; blue/pink/red flowers; gold highlighting	100	25.00	35.00	18.00

STYLE 2   WIDE LID, LOOPED HANDLE

BLUE DRESDEN DESIGN

Backstamp: Printed "The Regency Collection Made in Fine Bone China by Wade England"

No.	Description	Colourways	Size	U.S. $	Can. $	U.K. £
1	Teapot, 1-cup	White; blue flowers; gold highlights	100	25.00	35.00	18.00

STYLE 3   SMALL LID, RIBBED SHOULDER

GRAPEVINE DESIGN

Backstamp: Printed "The Regency Collection Made in Fine Bone China by Wade England"

No.	Description	Colourways	Size	U.S. $	Can. $	U.K. £
1	Teapot, 1-cup	White; black grapes; green leaves; gold highlighting	100	25.00	35.00	18.00

SAMANTHA SHAPE, 1988-1995

For complete sets in the Samantha Shape see pages 136-138.

CHARLOTTE DESIGN

Backstamp: Printed "Charlotte Wade England"

No.	Description	Colourways	Size	U.S. $	Can. $	U.K. £
1	Teapot, 4-cup	White; small red flowers; green leaves	140	25.00	35.00	18.00

CONTRASTS DESIGN

Backstamp: Printed "Wade England" between two lines

No.	Description	Colourways	Size	U.S. $	Can. $	U.K. £
1a	Teapot, 4-cup	Dusky pink; creamy white speckles	140	20.00	30.00	15.00
1b	Teapot, 4-cup	Pale grey; creamy white speckles	140	20.00	30.00	15.00
1c	Teapot, 4-cup	Pale pinky orange; creamy white speckles	140	20.00	30.00	15.00
1d	Teapot, 4-cup	Royal blue; creamy white speckles	140	20.00	30.00	15.00
1e	Teapot, 4-cup	Sugar pink; creamy white speckles	140	20.00	30.00	15.00
1f	Teapot, 4-cup	Tan; creamy white speckles	140	20.00	30.00	15.00

S
A
M
A
N
T
H
A

ROSE DESIGN

SAMANTHA

Backstamp: Printed "Rose Wade England"

No.	Description	Colourways	Size	U.S. $	Can. $	U.K. £
1	Teapot, 4-cup	White; large pink roses; green leaves	140	25.00	35.00	18.00

SELBY SHAPE, 1930

This shape was first advertised in *The Pottery and Glass Trades Review* in February 1930. For sets in this shape see pages 139-141.

BIRD, BUTTERFLIES AND FLOWERS DESIGN

Photograph of this
design not available
at press time

Backstamp: Orange ink stamp "Wades England" with lion

No.	Description	Colourways	Size	U.S. $	Can. $	U.K. £
1	Teapot, 4-cup	White; multi-coloured bird/butterflies/flowers	140	85.00	110.00	60.00

BLUE DESIGN

Backstamp: Orange ink stamp "Wades England" with lion

No.	Description	Colourways	Size	U.S. $	Can. $	U.K. £
1	Teapot, 4-cup	Royal blue; gold neck, spout tip	140	70.00	90.00	45.00

SELBY

GOLD SWIRLS DESIGN

Backstamp: Orange ink stamp "Wades England" with lion (1927-1933)

No.	Description	Colourways	Size	U.S. $	Can. $	U.K. £
1	Teapot, 6-cup	Royal blue; white neck; gold swirls	177	55.00	70.00	35.00

PAISLEY DESIGN

Backstamp: Orange ink stamp "Wades England" with lion (1927-1933)

No.	Description	Colourways	Size	U.S. $	Can. $	U.K. £
1	Teapot, 4-cup	Paisley chintz	140	175.00	200.00	100.00

TRADITIONAL SHAPE, 1987-1995

STYLE 1   DOMED LID, HANDLE WITHOUT THUMBREST

CHERRIES DESIGN

Backstamp: A. Blue printed circular frame "Royal Victoria Pottery Fine Bone China Wade England"
B. Printed semi-circular "Royal Victoria Pottery Wade England"

No.	Description	Colourways	Size	U.S. $	Can. $	U.K. £
1	Mug	White; black/red cherries; green leaves	95	3.00	4.00	2.00
2	Teapot, 6-cup		160	25.00	35.00	18.00
3	Teapot, 4-cup		140	18.00	25.00	12.00

FLORAL FAYRE DESIGN

Backstamp: A. Blue printed circular frame "Royal Victoria Pottery Fine Bone China Wade England"
B. Printed "Floral Fayre Wade England"

No.	Description	Colourways	Size	U.S. $	Can. $	U.K. £
1	Mug	White; pale pink flowers; grey green leaves	95	3.00	4.00	2.00
2	Teapot, 6-cup		160	25.00	35.00	18.00

FUSCHIA DESIGN

Backstamp: A. Blue printed circular frame "Royal Victoria Pottery Fine Bone China Wade England"
B. Printed "Fuchsia Wade England"

No.	Description	Colourways	Size	U.S. $	Can. $	U.K. £
1	Mug	White; yellow/pink flowers; grey leaves	95	3.00	4.00	2.00
2	Teapot, 6-cup		160	25.00	35.00	18.00

GERANIUM DESIGN

Backstamp: Printed "Geranium Wade England"

No.	Description	Colourways	Size	U.S. $	Can. $	U.K. £
1	Mug	White; pink/yellow/blue flowers; green leaves	95	3.00	4.00	2.00
2	Teapot, 6-cup		160	25.00	35.00	18.00
3	Teapot, 4-cup		140	18.00	25.00	12.00

IRIS DESIGN

TRADITIONAL

Backstamp: Blue printed circular frame "Royal Victoria Pottery Fine Bone China Wade England"

No.	Description	Colourways	Size	U.S. $	Can. $	U.K. £
1	Mug	White; mauve flowers; green leaves	95	3.00	4.00	2.00
2	Teapot, 6-cup		160	25.00	35.00	18.00

STRAWBERRIES DESIGN

Backstamp: **A.** Blue printed circular frame "Royal Victoria Pottery Fine Bone China Wade England"
   B. Printed semi-circular "Royal Victoria Pottery Wade England"

No.	Description	Colourways	Size	U.S. $	Can. $	U.K. £
1	Mug	White; red berries; white flowers; green leaves	95	3.00	4.00	2.00
2	Teapot, 6-cup		160	25.00	35.00	18.00
3	Teapot, 4-cup		140	18.00	25.00	12.00

TEAPOTS • 229

SWEET PEA DESIGN

Photograph of this
design not available
at press time

Backstamp: Blue printed circular frame "Royal Victoria Pottery Fine Bone China Wade England"

No.	Description	Colourways	Size	U.S. $	Can. $	U.K. £
1	Mug	White; mauve/pink/yellow flowers; green leaves	95	3.00	4.00	2.00
2	Teapot, 6-cup		160	25.00	35.00	18.00

WILD VIOLETS DESIGN

For an illustration
of this design
see below

Backstamp: Blue printed circular frame "Royal Victoria Pottery Fine Bone China Wade England"

No.	Description	Colourways	Size	U.S. $	Can. $	U.K. £
1	Mug	White; mauve/pink flowers; green leaves	95	3.00	4.00	2.00
2	Teapot, 6-cup		160	25.00	35.00	18.00

STYLE 2   FLAT LID, HANDLE WITH THUMBREST

WILD VIOLETS DESIGN

Backstamp: Printed semi-circular "Royal Victoria Pottery Wade England"

No.	Description	Colourways	Size	U.S. $	Can. $	U.K. £
1	Mug	White; blue/pink flowers; green leaves	95	3.00	4.00	2.00
2	Teapot, 5-cup		150	25.00	35.00	18.00
3	Teapot, 2-cup		120	18.00	25.00	12.00

TRADITIONAL

WINDSOR SHAPE, 1937-1940

STYLE 1   *SMOOTH BODY*

CROWN DERBY DESIGN

Backstamp: Red ink stamp "Wades England" with lion (1927-1933)

No.	Description	Colourways	Size	U.S. $	Can. $	U.K. £
1	Teapot, 4-cup	White; cobalt blue/gold handle and spout; gold neck; cobalt blue panels with gold decoration on top half; orange/blue and gold decoration on bottom	140	95.00	130.00	65.00

WINDSOR

STYLE 2   RIBBED BODY

BANDED DESIGN

Photograph of this
design not available
at press time

Backstamp: Black ink stamp "Wadeheath England" with lion and impressed "Made in England" (1934-1937)

No.	Description	Colourways	Size	U.S. $	Can. $	U.K. £
1	Teapot, 6-cup	White; green/yellow/grey bands	160	75.00	100.00	50.00

MOTTLED AND SOLID COLOURS DESIGN

Backstamp: Black ink stamp "Wadeheath England" with lion and impressed "Made in England" (1934-1937)

No.	Description	Colourways	Size	U.S. $	Can. $	U.K. £
1a	Teapot, 6-cup	Mottled orange/cream	160	75.00	100.00	50.00
1b	Teapot, 6-cup	Pale green	160	75.00	100.00	50.00
2	Teapot, 4-cup	Pale blue	140	75.00	100.00	50.00

WINDSOR

STYLE 3   RIBBED BODY WITH EMBOSSED FLOWERS

EMBOSSED FLOWERS DESIGN

Backstamp: Black ink stamp "Wade Heath England" with impressed "Made in England" (round W 1937-1940)

No.	Description	Colourways	Size	U.S. $	Can. $	U.K. £
1a	Teapot, 6-cup	Green/pale green; dark green leaves; maroon/yellow/ purple flowers	160	80.00	105.00	55.00
1b	Teapot, 6-cup	White/off-white; dark green leaves; maroon/ yellow/ purple flowers	160	80.00	105.00	55.00

SOLID COLOURS DESIGN

Backstamp: Green ink stamp "Wade Heath England J" with impressed "Made in England" (round W 1939-1945)

No.	Description	Colourways	Size	U.S. $	Can. $	U.K. £
1a	Teapot, 4-cup	Blue	140	60.00	80.00	40.00
1b	Teapot, 4-cup	Off white	140	60.00	80.00	40.00

UNKNOWN SHAPES

COUNTRYMEN ENGLISH COACHING INN DESIGN, c.1980

This teapot is a larger version of the Prince Charles and Lady Diana Wedding teapot which was first produced by Wade Ireland in 1981 (see *The Charlton Standard Catalogue of Wade Volume One: General Issues*). The decoration is of an Old English Coach House.

Photograph of this
design not available
at press time

Backstamp: Printed "Genuine Wade Porcelain" (c.1982)

No.	Description	Colourways	Size	U.S. $	Can. $	U.K. £
1	Coaching Inn teapot, 6-cup	White pot; multi-coloured print "The Old Coach House, York"	160	22.00	30.00	15.00

DAISY FLOWERS DESIGN

The shape name of the following teapots is unknown. The handle and shape of the teapots are similar to the octagonal Bee teapot but this shape teapot has smooth sides.

Backstamp: Black ink stamp "Wadeheath England" with lion (1933-1937)

No.	Description	Colourways	Size	U.S. $	Can. $	U.K. £
1	Teapot, 4-cup	Brown lid, neck, handle, spout, stripes; cream body; purple/yellow/blue flowers; green/black leaves	140	55.00	80.00	40.00

TULIPS AND POPPIES DESIGN

UNKNOWN

Backstamp: Black ink stamp "Wadeheath England" with lion (1933-1937)

No.	Description	Colourways	Size	U.S. $	Can. $	U.K. £
1	Teapot, 4-cup	White; yellow/orange red flowers; green leaves/streaks	140	55.00	80.00	40.00

Noveltyware

There are two sub-sections within this chapter. The first section includes those teapots and mugs that are "one-offs," that is, belonging to neither a set nor a series. The second section includes those teapots and miscellaneous pieces that are part of a larger series, for example the English Life Series.

SHAPE NAME INDEX

DRUMMER BOY SHAPE, 1991

This drum shaped teapot with a seated toy soldier forming the finial of the lid was produced for the Christmas season in 1991 for Boots the Chemist with an original price of £12.99.

Backstamp: Printed "Drummer Boy Designed Exclusively for Boots by Judith Wootton Wade" with two lines

No.	Description	Colourways	Size	U.S. $	Can. $	U.K. £
1	Teapot	Red/white drum; dark blue/red soldier finial on lid	165	60.00	80.00	40.00

GENIE SHAPE, 1990 - 1995

The first of these two Genie teapots was introduced in 1990 and decorated in copper lustre, the second, introduced in 1991, had a yellow background with copper lustre tints.

Backstamp: Printed "The Genie Teapot Made by Wade England" with two lines

No.	Description	Colourways	Size	U.S. $	Can. $	U.K. £
1a	Teapot	Copper lustre; cream genie with green turban; black beard; dark red waistcoat	216	105.00	140.00	70.00
1b	Teapot	Yellow; copper lustre; cream genie with green turban; black beard; dark red waistcoat	216	75.00	100.00	50.00

HORSE SHAPE, 1991-1992

DRESSAGE, 1992

This novelty teapot, produced for Boots the Chemist, is shaped as a horse with a number 67 rosette on his bridle. A woman in a 1930s riding habit forms the lid.

Backstamp: Printed "Dressage Designed Exclusively by Wade" with two lines and print of teapot

No.	Description	Colourways	Size	U.S. $	Can. $	U.K.£
1	Teapot	White horse; black hooves; female rider with black hat/riding habit	170	60.00	80.00	40.00

GYMKHANA PONY, 1991

This novelty teapot was produced for Boots the Chemist with an original price of £12.99.

Backstamp: Printed "Gymkhana Designed Exclusively for Boots by Judith Wootton Wade" with two lines and print of teapot

No.	Description	Colourways	Size	U.S. $	Can. $	U.K. £
1	Teapot	Grey horse; black hooves; child with black hat, red jacket and white jodhpurs	159	60.00	80.00	40.00

JUNGLE FUN ELEPHANT SHAPE, 1990

This set was produced for Boots the Chemist.

Backstamp: A. Printed "Jungle Fun Designed Exclusively for Boots by Wade Ceramics"
   B. Embossed "Wade England"
   C. Printed "Jungle Fun Wade England"

No.	Description	Colourways	Size	U.S. $	Can. $	U.K. £
1	Mug	White; multi-coloured print of jungle animals	95	4.00	6.00	3.00
2	Teapot		200	45.00	60.00	30.00

MOTHER DUCK SHAPE, 1936

This unique teapot is shaped as a mother duck, with a duckling on her back forming the lid. Noveltio was a British export company exporting British products, including Wade, to North America during the late 1940s and 1950s.

Backstamp: A. Green ink stamp "Wade Heath England" (round W 1937-c.1945)
   B. Green ink stamp "Noveltio made in England" (c.1940-c.1950)

No.	Description	Colourways	Size	U.S. $	Can. $	U.K. £
1	Teapot	Yellow duck; orange beak, feet; green-edged wing feathers	127	225.00	300.00	150.00

MOUNTAIN SHAPE, 1991 - 1993

Backstamp: Printed "Wade England" with two lines

No.	Description	Colourways	Size	U.S. $	Can. $	U.K. £
1a	"Après ski" teapot	White; multi-coloured print; lettering "Après Ski Teapot"	140	22.00	30.00	15.00
1b	"A Santa's Christmas" teapot	White; multi-coloured print; lettering "A Santa's Christmas Teapot"	140	22.00	30.00	15.00

NEST SHAPE, c. 1930

This embossed teapot has a tree branch and round petalled flowers design. Branches form the handle and spout. The lid is a bird's nest with four chicks, two with their beaks open the others shut, and a mother bird forms the finial.

Backstamp: Ink stamp "Wade Heath England"

No.	Description	Colourways	Size	U.S. $	Can. $	U.K. £
1	Teapot	Cream pot; brown handle, spout; green leaves; maroon/yellow/purple flowers; cream/purple birds; yellow beaks	153	140.00	190.00	95.00

NOAH'S ARK SHAPE, 1990

This ark shaped teapot and two matching mugs were produced for Boots the Chemist.

Backstamp: Printed "Designed Exclusively for Boots by Wade Ceramics"

No.	Description	Colourways	Size	U.S. $	Can. $	U.K. £
1a	Mug	White; multi-coloured animals	95	4.00	6.00	3.00
1b	Mug	White; multi-coloured Noah, animals, rainbow	95	4.00	6.00	3.00
2	Teapot	White; multi-coloured animals	127	40.00	60.00	30.00

PEASANT WOMAN SHAPE, 1991

Backstamp: Printed "Wade England" with two lines

No.	Description	Colourways	Size	U.S. $	Can. $	U.K. £
1	Biscuit Barrel	White; orange hair; orange/yellow bow; green leaves on shoes	266	55.00	70.00	35.00
2	Teapot	White; orange hair; red/blue collar; red/blue flowered apron; blue/red diamond on shoes	165	45.00	60.00	30.00

RINGMASTER TENT SHAPE, 1990

This circus tent shaped teapot was produced exclusively for Boots the Chemist with a matching mug. Two backstamps have been found on this teapot.

Backstamp: **A.** Printed "Made in England"
B. Printed "Designed Exclusively for Boots by Wade Ceramics"

No.	Description	Colourways	Size	U.S. $	Can. $	U.K. £
1	Mug	White; multi-coloured circus print	95	4.00	6.00	3.00
2	Teapot		127	22.00	30.00	15.00

SNOOKER PLAYER SHAPE, 1994

The finial of the lid of this snooker ball shaped teapot is a player leaning over the table to make a shot.

Backstamp: Large embossed "Wade England"

No.	Description	Colourways	Size	U.S. $	Can. $	U.K. £
1	Teapot	Black; white shirt, cue stick; black waistcoat, trousers	185	65.00	85.00	45.00

WADELAND FIRE ENGINE COMPANY SHAPE, 1993

Backstamp: Printed "Wade England" with two lines

No.	Description	Colourways	Size	U.S. $	Can. $	U.K. £
1	Teapot	White; multi-coloured print; red lettering	125	30.00	40.00	20.00

WHITE RABBIT SHAPE, 1992

Produced in 1992 for Boots the Chemist, this novelty teapot had an original selling price of £12.99

Backstamp: Printed "White Rabbit Designed Exclusively by Wade" with two lines

No.	Description	Colourways	Size	U.S. $	Can. $	U.K. £
1	Teapot	White; red/white squares; red heart design; blue spout tip	210	65.00	85.00	35.00

EXTRA LARGE CUPS AND SAUCERS, 1991 - 1995

These novelty cups and saucers were produced for Boots the Chemist.

Backstamp **A.** Black printed "Wade England" with two lines
B. Embossed "Wade England"

No.	Description	Colourways	Size	U.S. $	Can. $	U.K. £
1a	"Cafe au Lait" Cup and saucer	Royal blue; gold lettering	90/170	18.00	24.00	12.00
1b	Comic Animals Cup and saucer	White; brown; black; dark green; grey print comic hedgehog, mole, rabbit & mouse	90/170	18.00	24.00	12.00
1c	"Good Morning" Cup and saucer	White; multi-coloured print of cockerel & sunrise; brown lettering	90/170	18.00	24.00	12.00
1d	"Home Sweet Home" Cup and saucer	White; multi-coloured house & garden print; blue lettering	90/170	18.00	24.00	12.00
1e	"I'm the boss" Cup and saucer	Black; white lettering "I'm the boss"	90/170	18.00	24.00	12.00

NOVELTYWARE SERIES

BEAR AMBITIONS SERIES, 1995 - 1996

There are two shapes of handles and lids on these teapots, three teapots have angled handles and domed lids that sit inside the top rim and the other three teapots have round handles and sloping lids that overlap the top rim. A set of six miniature Bear Ambition models were also produced by Wade (see The *Charlton Standard Catalogue of Wade Whimsicals*, 4th edition).

STYLE 1   ANGLED HANDLE

Artistic Edward   Musical Marco

Backstamp: Printed "Designed by Judith Wooton Wade" with the name and story of the character portrayed

No.	Description	Colourways	Size	U.S. $	Can. $	U.K. £
1a	Artistic Edward teapot	White; multi-coloured print	165	40.00	50.00	25.00
1b	Beatrice Ballerina teapot		165	40.00	50.00	25.00
1c	Musical Marco teapot		165	40.00	50.00	25.00

STYLE 2   ROUND HANDLE

Locomotive Joe

Backstamp: Printed "Wade" with the name and story of the character portrayed

No.	Description	Colourways	Size	U.S. $	Can. $	U.K. £
2a	Admiral Sam teapot	White; multi-coloured print	165	40.00	50.00	25.00
2b	Alex the Aviator teapot		165	40.00	50.00	25.00
2c	Locomotive Joe teapot		165	40.00	50.00	25.00

THE CHRISTMAS COLLECTION SERIES, 1989 - 1991

CHRISTMAS CAROL DESIGN, 1990

Backstamp: A. Printed "The Christmas Collection made by Wade England" with two lines
B. Printed "Wade England" with two lines

No.	Description	Colourways	Size	U.S. $	Can. $	U.K. £
1	Teapot	White; multi-coloured print; black lettering "Merry Christmas"	153	22.00	30.00	15.00

CHRISTMAS MUG DESIGN, 1991

A coffee mug with a transfer print of a Christmas scene with a fireplace and decorations, the reverse of the mug shows a Christmas morning scene with a child and Christmas tree.

Backstamp: Printed "Wade England" with two lines (1990)

No.	Description	Colourways	Size	U.S. $	Can. $	U.K. £
1	Mug	White; multi-coloured prints; black lettering "Christmas "	95	4.00	6.00	3.00

CHRISTMAS TREE DESIGN, 1990-1991

Backstamp: Printed "Wade England" with two lines

No.	Description	Colourways	Size	U.S. $	Can. $	U.K. £
1a	Teapot	Green; gold star; multi-coloured print; "A Christmas Teapot"	146	30.00	40.00	20.00
1b	Teapot	Dark green; gold star; multi-coloured print; "A Happy Christmas Teapot"	146	30.00	40.00	20.00
1c	Teapot	White; gold star; multi-coloured print; "A Merry Christmas Teapot"	146	30.00	40.00	20.00
1d	Teapot	White; gold star; Fleur-de-Lis	146	22.00	30.00	15.00
1e	Teapot	Green; gold star; Fleur-de-Lis	146	22.00	30.00	15.00

SANTA'S GROTTO DESIGN, 1989

Backstamp: Printed "The Christmas Collection No 1 Santas Grotto Made by Wade Potteries PLC"

No.	Description	Colourways	Size	U.S. $	Can. $	U.K. £
1	Teapot	White; multi-coloured print; black lettering "Merry Christmas Santa's Grotto"	153	22.00	30.00	15.00

CHRISTMAS

COCKLESHELL COVE SERIES, 1990 - 1993

This set of teapots with a seaside theme was produced in 1990 with the matching mugs being added in 1993. The shape and decoration of the teapot is reflected in the name of the piece.

Henry's Helter Skelter

La Bellavista Guest House

Punch and Judy Show

Lighthouse

Backstamp: Printed "Wade England" with two lines

No.	Description	Colourways	Size	U.S. $	Can. $	U.K. £
1a	Mug	White; multi-coloured print; "Henry's Helter Skelter"	95	4.00	6.00	3.00
1b	Mug	White; multi-coloured print; "La Bellavista Guest House"	95	4.00	6.00	3.00
1c	Mug	White; multi-coloured print, "Punch and Judy Show"	95	4.00	6.00	3.00
2	Teapot	White; green lid with red/blue/yellow dots; multi-coloured print; blue lettering "Cockleshell Pier Theatre"	159	30.00	40.00	20.00
3	Teapot	White; multi-coloured print; red lettering "Henry's Helter Skelter"	190	40.00	55.00	25.00
4	Teapot	White; multi-coloured print; black lettering "La Bellavista Guest House"	195	30.00	40.00	20.00
5	Teapot	Yellow; multi-coloured print; yellow lettering "Punch and Judy Show Next Show 2pm"	Unknown	30.00	40.00	20.00
6	Teapot	White/red striped; black/grey lid; multi-coloured print of a lighthouse	190	35.00	45.00	22.00

ENGLISH LIFE SERIES, 1989 - 1993

The first six teapots in the English Life Series were advertised as Victorian Style Designs in January 1989. Most of the teapots, with the exception of the Conservatory teapot, are square and in the shape of typical English buildings. They are white, with multi-coloured transfer prints of windows, doors and people, with the roof of each building serving as the teapot lid. Tea caddies, mugs, plates (see Plaques and Wall Decorations section in *The Charlton Standard Catalogue of Wade, Volume Two: Decorative Ware*), a sugar canister and a milk jug were added to the series. The tin caddies were filled with 50 grams of tea and were produced by Wade pdm in conjunction with Avon Tin printers.

ANTIQUE SHOP DESIGN, 1989-1993

Backstamp: **A.** Grey printed ""English Life Teapots, Designs by Barry Smith and Barbara Wootton exclusively for Wade England" (1989-1993)
B. Printed "Wade England" with two lines (1992-1993) (on mugs)
C. Black printed "English life Tea Caddies, Designs by Barry Smith and Barbara Wootton exclusively for Wade England" (1991-1993)

No.	Description	Colourways	Size	U.S. $	Can. $	U.K. £
1	Caddy, ceramic	White; multi-coloured print; black/grey lettering "Antiques/an antique tea caddy"	133	14.00	18.00	9.00
2	Caddy, tin	White; multi-coloured print; black lettering "Antiques/an antique tea caddy"	105	8.00	10.00	5.00
3	Mug	White; multi-coloured print; black/grey lettering "Antiques"	95	4.00	6.00	3.00
4	Teapot	Pointed roof with centre portrait; multi-colour prints; black/grey lettering "Antiques/an antique teapot"	146	25.00	30.00	15.00

E N G L I S H   L I F E

CONSERVATORY DESIGN, 1989-1993

Backstamp: A. Grey printed "English Life Teapots, Designs by Barry Smith and Barbara Wootton, exclusively for Wade England" (1989-1993)
B. Printed "Wade England" with two lines (1992-1993) (on mugs)
C. Black printed "English life Tea Caddies, Designs by Barry Smith and Barbara Wootton exclusively for Wade England" (1989-1993)
D. Black printed "An exclusive teapot designed by Matthew Walker made by Wade England"

No.	Description	Colourways	Size	U.S. $	Can. $	U.K. £
1	Caddy	White; multi-coloured print; black/grey lettering "A conservatory tea caddy"	114	14.00	18.00	9.00
2	Mug	White; multi-coloured print; black/grey lettering "A conservatory mug"	95	4.00	6.00	3.00
3a	Teapot	Pointed roof; multi-coloured print of flowers/vegetables; black/grey lettering "A conservatory teapot"	133	25.00	30.00	15.00
3b	Teapot	Pointed roof; multi-coloured print of plants, people, macaw; black/grey lettering "A conservatory teapot	133	30.00	36.00	18.00

CRICKET DESIGN, 1991

Backstamp: Printed "English Life Teapots made by Wade England" with two lines (1991)

No.	Description	Colourways	Size	U.S. $	Can. $	U.K. £
1	Teapot	Apex roof, brown/yellow "woven" tile, black beams/ clock, white pot; multi-coloured print	150	30.00	40.00	20.00

FISH AND CHIP SHOP DESIGN, 1990-1993

Backstamp: A. Printed "Wade England" with two lines (1992-1993) (on mugs)
B. Printed "English Life Teapots made by Wade England" with two lines (1990-1993)

No.	Description	Colourways	Size	U.S. $	Can. $	U.K. £
1	Mug	White; multi-coloured print; grey/yellow lettering "1881 Fish and Chip Shop"	95	4.00	6.00	3.00
2	Teapot	Apex roof, green/grey fish scales; multi-coloured prints; black/yellow lettering "Fish and Chip Shop a chip shop teapot"	146	25.00	30.00	15.00

FISHMONGERS DESIGN, 1990-1993

Backstamp: **A.** Printed "Wade England" with two lines (1990-1993) (on mugs)
B. Printed "English Life Teapots made by Wade England" with two lines (1990-1993)

No.	Description	Colourways	Size	U.S. $	Can. $	U.K. £
1	Mug	White; multi-coloured print; black/grey lettering "Fishmongers Fresh Fish Daily	95	4.00	6.00	3.00
2	Teapot	Domed roof, fish and oyster shells round edges; multi-coloured prints; black/grey lettering "J. Herring and Son Fishmongers Fresh Fish Daily a fishmongers teapot"	153	25.00	30.00	15.00

FLORIE'S FLOWERS DESIGN, 1989-1993

Backstamp: **A.** Grey printed "English Life Teapots, Designs by Barry Smith and Barbara Wootton, exclusively for Wade England" (1989-1993)
B. Printed "Wade England" with two lines (1992-1993) (on mugs)

No.	Description	Colourways	Size	U.S. $	Can. $	U.K. £
1	Mug	White; multi-coloured print; grey lettering "Florie's Flowers"	95	4.00	6.00	3.00
2	Teapot	Domed roof; green tree leaves on roof; multi-colour prints; black/grey lettering "Florie's Flowers a floral teapot"	140	25.00	30.00	15.00

PET SHOP DESIGN, 1990-1993

Backstamp: **A.** Printed "Wade England" with two lines (1992-1993) (on mugs)
B. Printed "English Life Teapots made by Wade England" with two lines (1990-1993)

No.	Description	Colourways	Size	U.S. $	Can. $	U.K. £
1	Mug	White; multi-coloured print; yellow/white lettering "Pet Shop Four Paws a pet shop mug"	95	4.00	6.00	3.00
2	Teapot	Rounded roof, windows with red curtains; multi-coloured prints; yellow/white/grey lettering "Pet Shop Four Paws a pet shop teapot"	132	25.00	30.00	15.00

POLICE STATION DESIGN, 1990-1993

Backstamp: A. Printed "Wade England" with two lines (1992-1993) (on mugs)
B. Printed "English Life Teapots made by Wade England" with two lines (1990-1993)

No.	Description	Colourways	Size	U.S. $	Can. $	U.K. £
1	Mug	White; multi-coloured print; grey lettering "A police station mug"	95	4.00	6.00	3.00
2	Teapot	Pointed roof, blue light dome on chimney; red tiles; multi-coloured prints; black/grey lettering "1904 A police station teapot"	160	25.00	30.00	15.00

POLLY'S CAFE DESIGN, 1990-1993

Backstamp: A. Grey printed "English Life Teapots, Designs by Barry Smith and Barbara Wootton, exclusively for Wade England" (1989-1993)
B. Printed "Wade England" with two lines (1992-1993) (on mugs)
C. Black printed "English life Tea Caddies, Designs by Barry Smith and Barbara Wootton exclusively for Wade England" (1991-1993)

No.	Description	Colourways	Size	U.S. $	Can. $	U.K. £
1	Caddy, ceramic	White; multi-coloured print; black/grey lettering "Polly's Teapot Cafe Home Made Sweets and Cakes a cafe tea caddy"	114	14.00	18.00	9.00
2	Mug	White; multi-coloured print; black/grey lettering "A cafe mug/Polly's Teapot Cafe Home Made Sweets and Cakes"	95	4.00	6.00	3.00
3a	Teapot	White; multi-coloured prints; black/red lettering "Polly's Teapot Cafe Home made Sweets and Cakes a cafe teapot"	127	25.00	30.00	15.00
3b	Teapot	White; multi-coloured prints; black/grey lettering "Polly's Teapot Cafe Light Teas and Snacks a cafe teapot"	127	25.00	30.00	15.00

POST OFFICE DESIGN, 1989-1993

Backstamp: **A.** Grey printed "English Life Teapots, Designs by Barry Smith and Barbara Wootton, exclusively for Wade England" (1989-1993)
  B. Printed "Wade England" with two lines (1992-1993) (on mugs)
  C. Black printed "English life Tea Caddies, Designs by Barry Smith and Barbara Wootton exclusively for Wade England" (1991-1993)

No.	Description	Colourways	Size	U.S. $	Can. $	U.K. £
1	Caddy, tin	White; multi-coloured print; black lettering "Post Office Est 1906 a first class tea caddy"	105	8.00	10.00	5.00
2	Mug	White; multi-coloured print; grey/red lettering "General Store Post Office Post Office Est 1906"	95	4.00	6.00	3.00
3	Teapot	Domed castellated roof; grey tile; square teapot; multi-colour prints; red/black/grey lettering "Post Office EST 1906 a first class teapot"	133	25.00	30.00	15.00

PRIMROSE JUNCTION DESIGN, 1989-1993

Backstamp: **A.** Grey printed "English Life Teapots, Designs by Barry Smith and Barbara Wootton, exclusively for Wade England" (1989-1993)
B. Printed "Wade England" with two lines (1992-1993) (on mugs)
C. Black printed "English life Tea Caddies, Designs by Barry Smith and Barbara Wootton exclusively for Wade England" (1991-1993)

No.	Description	Colourways	Size	U.S. $	Can. $	U.K. £
1	Caddy, tin	White; multi-coloured print; black lettering "Railway station tea caddy Primrose Junction a railway tea caddy"	105	8.00	10.00	5.00
2	Mug	White; multi-coloured print; black/grey lettering "A railway station mug Primrose Junction"	95	4.00	6.00	3.00
3	Teapot	Pointed roof; grey tiles/clock; multi-colour prints; black/grey lettering "Primrose Junction a railway station teapot"	140	20.00	30.00	15.00

SWEET SHOP AND VILLAGE DAIRY DESIGN, 1989

This cream and sugar were sold as a boxed set of two, or as a set of three with one of the Village Life teapots.

Backstamp: Grey printed "English Life Designs by Barry Smith and Barbara Wootton exclusively for Wade England" (1989-1993)

No.	Description	Colourways	Size	U.S. $	Can. $	U.K. £
1	Milk jug	White; multi-coloured prints; black/grey lettering "Village Dairy a village milk jug"	70	12.00	15.00	8.00
2	Sugar bowl	White/grey lid; multi-coloured prints; black/grey lettering "Sweet Sues Sweet Shop Hand made Confection a sweet shop sugar bowl"	85	14.00	18.00	9.00

QUEEN VICTORIA PUB DESIGN, 1989-1993

Backstamp: **A.** Grey printed "English Life Teapots, Designs by Barry Smith and Barbara Wootton,
exclusively for Wade England" (1989-1993)
B. Printed "Wade England" with two lines (1992-1993) (on mugs)
C. Black printed "English life Tea Caddies, Designs by Barry Smith and Barbara Wootton
exclusively for Wade England" (1991-1993)

No.	Description	Colourways	Size	U.S. $	Can. $	U.K. £
1	Caddy, ceramic	White; multi-coloured print; black/grey lettering "The Queen Victoria a pub tea caddy"	133	14.00	18.00	9.00
2	Caddy, tin	White; multi-coloured print; black lettering "The Queen Victoria and a pub tea caddy"	105	8.00	10.00	5.00
3	Mug	White; multi-coloured print; black lettering "The Queen Victoria"	95	4.00	6.00	3.00
4	Teapot	Pointed roof with four corner bricks, grey tiles; multi-coloured prints; black/grey lettering "The Queen Victoria a pub teapot"	146	25.00	30.00	15.00

T. POTTS CHINA SHOP DESIGN, 1990-1993

Backstamp: **A.** Printed "Wade England" with two lines (1992-1993) (on mugs)
B. Printed "English Life Teapots made by Wade England" with two lines (1990-1993)

No.	Description	Colourways	Size	U.S. $	Can. $	U.K. £
1	Mug	White; multi-coloured print; black/blue lettering "Est 1863 T. Potts China Shop"	95	4.00	6.00	3.00
2	Teapot	Apex roof; grey tile; yellow window; multi-coloured prints; black/blue lettering"Est 1863 T. Potts China Shop a china shop teapot"	153	25.00	30.00	15.00

WEDDING DESIGN

Backstamp: Printed "Village Events The Wedding Teapot Wade England" with two lines

No.	Description	Colourways	Size	U.S. $	Can. $	U.K. £
1	Teapot	White; arched roof, stain glass windows, multi-coloured print	171	30.00	40.00	20.00

LONDON LIFE SERIES, 1995

Backstamp: Printed "Wade London Life Made in England designed by Barbara Cooksey"

No.	Description	Colourways	Size	U.S. $	Can. $	U.K. £
1a	The Capital teapot	White teapot; multi-coloured print	171	40.00	50.00	25.00
1b	The Guards teapot		171	40.00	50.00	25.00
1c	On Parade teapot		171	40.00	50.00	25.00

MEMORIES SERIES, 1992-1993

These teapots are based on an English nursery rhyme: "The Owl and the Pussy Cat went to sea in a beautiful pea green boat, they took some honey and plenty of money wrapped up in a five pound note." Which is why the teapots were produced in aqua blue, pea green and honey glazes with a five pound note as the finial.

Backstamp: Embossed "Wade England"

No.	Description	Colourways	Size	U.S. $	Can. $	U.K. £
1a	Cat teapot	Aqua blue	140	45.00	60.00	30.00
1b	Cat teapot	Pea green	140	45.00	60.00	30.00
2	Owl teapot	Honey	140	45.00	60.00	30.00

WHIMSICAL FELINES SERIES, 1989-1992

W
H
I
M
S
I
C
A
L

F
E
L
I
N
E
S

Cat Fish

Cat Litter

Cat Nap

CAT FISH DESIGN

Backstamp: Printed "Whimsical Teapots, Feline collection, Designed by Judith Wooton, Wade England"

No.	Description	Colourways	Size	U.S. $	Can. $	U.K. £
1	Teapot, large	Pale blue goldfish bowl; blue/black marked cat; multi-coloured transfer print of goldfish and water weed	130	40.00	50.00	25.00
2	Teapot, small		120	30.00	40.00	20.00

CAT LITTER DESIGN

Backstamp: Printed "Whimsical Teapots, Feline collection, Designed by Judith Wooton, Wade England"

No.	Description	Colourways	Size	U.S. $	Can. $	U.K. £
1	Teapot, large	Grey dustbin; brown and grey cat on lid; multi-coloured print of cats amongst litter/garbage	155	40.00	50.00	25.00
2	Teapot, small		140	30.00	40.00	20.00

CAT NAP DESIGN

Backstamp: Printed "Whimsical Teapots, Feline collection, Designed by Judith Wooton, Wade England"

No.	Description	Colourways	Size	U.S. $	Can. $	U.K. £
1	Teapot, large	White arm chair; yellow/blue/red flowers; black/white cats	165	40.00	50.00	25.00
2	Teapot, small		150	30.00	40.00	20.00

Stands For Teapots
c.1940-c.1970

While some stands for teapots were produced with matching teapots and hot water jugs (see Sets section), those listed here have no matching items and were produced as giftware.

SHAPE NAME INDEX

WADE IRELAND

IRISH WADE SHAPE NO. IP 624

Galleon

Irish Kitchen

Stags Head

W A D E   I R E L A N D

Backstamp: A. Impressed "Irish Porcelain (curved over shamrock) Made in Ireland By Wade Co. Armagh"
B. Embossed "Made in Ireland By Wade"

No.	Description	Colourways	Size	U.S. $	Can. $	U.K. £
1a	Carnations	Blue green tile; pink print	140	22.00	30.00	15.00
1b	Colleen carrying peat	Blue green tile; grey/red print	140	30.00	40.00	20.00
1c	Finn McCaul	Blue green tile; grey/red print	140	30.00	40.00	20.00
1d	Fox hunter	Blue green tile; grey/red print	140	30.00	40.00	20.00
1e	Galleon	Blue grey green tile; brown galleon; green sails	140	25.00	35.00	18.00
1f	Irish kitchen	Blue green tile; multi-coloured print	140	30.00	40.00	20.00
1g	Piccadilly Circus	Blue green tile; multi-coloured print	140	30.00	40.00	20.00
1h	Stags head	Blue green tile; white/brown print	140	30.00	40.00	20.00

VERSES DESIGN

Backstamp: A. Impressed "Irish Porcelain (curved over shamrock) Made in Ireland By Wade Co. Armagh"
B. Embossed "Made in Ireland By Wade"

No.	Description	Colourways	Size	U.S. $	Can. $	U.K. £
1a	Friendship	White tile; yellow roses; black lettering	140	30.00	40.00	20.00
1b	Home	White tile; yellow roses; black lettering	140	30.00	40.00	20.00
1c	Kindness	Cream tile; pink roses; black lettering	140	30.00	40.00	20.00
1d	"There's no place like home"	Cream tile; pink roses; black lettering	140	30.00	40.00	20.00

WADE ENGLAND

PEONIES DESIGN, c. 1940–c. 1952

This hand-painted design was used many times on bowls, dishes and other decorative wares.

Photograph of this
design not available
at press time

Backstamp: Ink stamp "Harvest Ware Wade England"

No.	Description	Colourways	Size	U.S. $	Can. $	U.K. £
1	Stand for teapot	Cream; copper rim; maroon/yellow flower; green/brown leaves	159	45.00	60.00	30.00

WADE IRELAND

Coffee Items and Sets

SHAPE NAME INDEX

IRISH WADE SHAPES, c.1950 - c.1980

IRISH COFFEE MUGS DESIGN, c.1978-1986
Irish Wade Shape No I.P. 44 , Irish Wade Shamrock Range Shape No. SR.16

Backstamp Impressed "Irish Porcelain (curved over large shamrock) Made in Ireland" in straight line

No.	Description	Colourways	Size	U.S. $	Can. $	U.K. £
1a	Beefeater coffee mug	Blue green; multi-coloured print	127	20.00	25.00	12.00
1b	Irish coffee mug	Blue green; gold lettering	127	20.00	25.00	12.00
1c	Shamrock coffee mug	White; gold lettering; green shamrocks	127	30.00	40.00	20.00

KNURLED DESIGN No. I.P. 100 / 101, c.1950, c.1970-c.1989

The cup has three rows of knurls and one row of shamrocks, and the saucer has one row of knurls and one row of shamrocks.

Backstamp: **A.** Embossed "Irish Porcelain (curved over shamrock) Made in Ireland by Wade Co. Armagh"
in straight lines (c.1953, c.1970-c.1989)
B. Embossed circular "Irish Porcelain (centre shamrock) Made in Ireland"
(with potters initial included) (c.1953, c.1970-c.1989)
C. Impressed "Irish Porcelain made in Ireland R" (c.1980)

No.	Description	Colourways	Size	U.S. $	Can. $	U.K. £
1	Cup and saucer	Blue grey	75/128	30.00	35.00	20.00

LONG KNURL DESIGN, c.1960

Backstamp: **A.** Embossed "Irish Porcelain by Wade Ireland Design by D.S. Nelson"
B. Printed circular "Made in Ireland Porcelain Wade eireir A dheanta"

No.	Description	Colourways	Size	U.S. $	Can. $	U.K. £
1	Coffee pot	Blue grey	266	55.00	70.00	35.00
2	Cup and saucer		76/146	22.00	30.00	15.00
3	Sugar bowl		138	40.00	50.00	25.00
4	Tea plate		160	15.00	20.00	10.00

IRISH WADE

RAINDROP DESIGN, c.1960 - c.1979

Version One — Pointed Drops, c.1970

Backstamp: A. Embossed oval "Irish Porcelain (over a small shamrock) Made in Ireland" in Irish knot wreath
B. Embossed circular "Made in Ireland Porcelain (central small shamrock and crown) Wade eire tira dheanta"

No.	Description	Colourways	Size	U.S. $	Can. $	U.K. £
1	Coffee pot	Blue grey	159	85.00	110.00	50.00
2	Cream jug		70	18.00	23.00	12.00
3	Milk jug, 1 pint		153	30.00	40.00	20.00
4	Milk jug, ¾ pint		114	22.00	30.00	15.00
5	Milk jug, ½ pint		101	22.00	30.00	15.00
6	Sugar bowl		50	15.00	18.00	10.00

Version Two — Round Drops, c.1960

For an illustration
of this design
see page 124

Backstamp: A. Embossed oval "Irish Porcelain (over a small shamrock) Made in Ireland" in Irish knot wreath
B. Embossed circular "Made in Ireland Porcelain (central small shamrock and crown) Wade eire tira dheanta"

No.	Description	Colourways	Size	U.S. $	Can. $	U.K. £
1	Coffee pot	Blue grey	159	85.00	110.00	50.00
2	Cream jug		70	18.00	23.00	12.00
3	Milk jug, 1 pint		153	30.00	40.00	20.00
4	Milk jug, ¾ pint		114	22.00	30.00	15.00
5	Milk jug, ½ pint		101	22.00	30.00	15.00
6	Sugar bowl		50	15.00	18.00	10.00

SHAMROCK DESIGN, c.1958-c.1962
Version One — Three footed, Shape No. I.P. 603

The three-footed sugar bowl was advertised as a posy bowl (see *The Charlton Standard Catalogue of Wade, Volume Two*, page 252) but was also used as a matching sugar bowl to this miniature three-footed cream jug.

Backstamp: Embossed circular "Irish Porcelain Made in Ireland" with small shamrock in centre (c.1950-c.1969)

No.	Description	Colourways	Size	U.S. $	Can. $	U.K. £
1	Footed cream jug	Blue green	50	12.00	15.00	8.00
2	Footed sugar bowl		60	12.00	15.00	8.00

SHAMROCK DESIGN, c.1970
Version Two — Flat base Shape Nos I.P.72/73 Irish Wade

This cream and sugar could be purchased in a pack with four Irish coffee glasses and a linen tea towel with a recipe for Irish Coffee, or with two Irish coffee glasses with the measurements of each ingredient marked on the glass.

Backstamp: Impressed circular "Irish Porcelain Made in Ireland" with a large shamrock in the centre (c.1953-c.1975)

No.	Description	Colourways	Size	U.S. $	Can. $	U.K. £
1	Cream jug	Blue green	50	10.00	12.00	6.00
2	Sugar bowl		40	10.00	12.00	6.00

REGENCY SHAPE, 1952-1961

BLACK AND GOLD INTERIOR DESIGN, 1961

Backstamp: Gold printed circular "Royal Victoria Pottery Wade England" (c.1960-c.1979)

No.	Description	Colourways	Size	U.S. $	Can. $	U.K. £
1	Coffee pot	Black and gold	170	50.00	70.00	30.00
2	Cream jug		50	12.00	15.00	8.00
3	Cup and saucer		60/120	15.00	20.00	10.00
4	Sugar bowl		43	12.00	15.00	8.00

FLORAL DESIGN

Backstamp: Gold printed "Wade Made in England Hand Painted" (1953-c.1960)

No.	Description	Colourways	Size	U.S. $	Can. $	U.K. £
1	Cream jug	Cream; gold trim; maroon flowers; green leaves	50	12.00	15.00	8.00
2	Sugar bowl, lidded		57	15.00	20.00	10.00

REGENCY

GOLD DESIGN

Backstamp: Gold printed circular "Royal Victoria Pottery Wade England" (c.1960-c.1979)

No.	Description	Colourways	Size	U.S. $	Can. $	U.K. £
1	Coffee pot	Gold	170	60.00	80.00	40.00
2	Cream jug		50	15.00	20.00	10.00
3	Cup and saucer		60/120	20.00	25.00	12.00
4	Sugar bowl		43	15.00	20.00	10.00

GOLD WITH WHITE INTERIOR DESIGN, 1961

Backstamp: Gold printed circular "Royal Victoria Pottery Wade England" (c.1960-c.1979)

No.	Description	Colourways	Size	U.S. $	Can. $	U.K. £
1	Coffee pot	Gold and white	170	60.00	80.00	40.00
2	Cream jug		50	15.00	20.00	10.00
3	Cup and saucer		60/120	20.00	25.00	12.00
4	Sugar bowl		43	15.00	20.00	10.00

HARLECH DESIGN

Backstamp: Black printed "Wade Harlech England" (c.1958-c.1962)

No.	Description	Colourways	Size	U.S. $	Can. $	U.K. £
1	Coffee pot	White; multi-coloured flowers and leaves	170	50.00	70.00	30.00
2	Cream jug		50	12.00	15.00	8.00
3	Cup and saucer		60/120	15.00	20.00	10.00
4	Sugar bowl		43	12.00	15.00	8.00

INDIAN TREE DESIGN, 1952

For an illustration
of this design
see page 112

Backstamp: Ink stamp "Wade England" (c.1948-1953)

No.	Description	Colourways	Size	U.S. $	Can. $	U.K. £
1	Coffee pot	White; brown tree; pink/yellow flowers	170	50.00	70.00	30.00
2	Cream jug		50	12.00	15.00	8.00
3	Cup and saucer		60/120	15.00	20.00	10.00
4	Sugar bowl		43	12.00	15.00	8.00

MAROON WITH GOLD INTERIOR DESIGN, 1961

Photograph of this
design not available
at press time

Backstamp: Gold printed circular "Royal Victoria Pottery Wade England" (c.1960-c.1979)

No.	Description	Colourways	Size	U.S. $	Can. $	U.K. £
1	Coffee pot	Maroon with gold interior	170	50.00	70.00	30.00
2	Cream jug		50	12.00	15.00	8.00
3	Cup and saucer		60/120	15.00	20.00	10.00
4	Sugar bowl		43	12.00	15.00	8.00

MOTHER OF PEARL WITH GOLD RIM DESIGN, 1961

Photograph of this
design not available
at press time

Backstamp: Gold printed circular "Royal Victoria Pottery Wade England" (c.1960-c.1979)

No.	Description	Colourways	Size	U.S. $	Can. $	U.K. £
1	Coffee pot	Mother of pearl with gold rim	170	50.00	70.00	30.00
2	Cream jug		50	12.00	15.00	8.00
3	Cup and saucer		60/120	15.00	20.00	10.00
4	Sugar bowl		43	12.00	15.00	8.00

PASTEL SPOTS DESIGN

Backstamp: Green ink stamp "Wade England"

No.	Description	Colourways	Size	U.S. $	Can. $	U.K. £
1	Cream jug	Cream jug; gold rim, handle; pastel pink, green, yellow spots	50	12.00	15.00	8.00

PINK WITH GOLD INTERIOR DESIGN, 1961

Photograph of this
design not available
at press time

Backstamp: Gold printed circular "Royal Victoria Pottery Wade England" (c.1960-c.1979)

No.	Description	Colourways	Size	U.S. $	Can. $	U.K. £
1	Coffee pot	Pink and gold	170	50.00	70.00	30.00
2	Cream jug		50	12.00	15.00	8.00
3	Cup and saucer		60/120	15.00	20.00	10.00
4	Sugar bowl		43	12.00	15.00	8.00

REGENCY

POPPY DESIGN, 1961

Backstamp: Green ink stamp "Wade England"

No.	Description	Colourways	Size	U.S. $	Can. $	U.K. £
1	Cup and saucer	Salmon pink; pinky red poppy flower; pale green/pink leaves	60/120	15.00	20.00	10.00

PRIMROSE WITH GOLD INTERIOR DESIGN, 1961

Photograph of this
design not available
at press time

Backstamp: Gold printed circular "Royal Victoria Pottery Wade England" (c.1960-c.1979)

No.	Description	Colourways	Size	U.S. $	Can. $	U.K. £
1	Coffee pot	Primrose and gold	170	50.00	70.00	30.00
2	Cream jug		50	12.00	15.00	8.00
3	Cup and saucer		60/120	15.00	20.00	10.00
4	Sugar bowl		43	12.00	15.00	8.00

TURQUOISE WITH GOLD INTERIOR DESIGN, 1961

Backstamp: Gold printed circular "Royal Victoria Pottery Wade England" (c.1960-c.1979)

No.	Description	Colourways	Size	U.S. $	Can. $	U.K. £
1	Coffee pot	Turquoise and gold	170	50.00	70.00	30.00
2	Cream jug		50	12.00	15.00	8.00
3	Cup and saucer		60/120	15.00	20.00	10.00
4	Sugar bowl		43	12.00	15.00	8.00

WINDSOR SHAPE, 1934-1937

BLUE DESIGN

Backstamp: Black ink stamp "Wadeheath England" with lion

No.	Description	Colourways	Size	U.S. $	Can. $	U.K. £
1	Coffee pot	Mottled blue/cream	192	75.00	100.00	50.00

GREEN BAND WITH FLOWERS DESIGN

Backstamp: Black ink stamp "Wadeheath England" with lion

No.	Description	Colourways	Size	U.S. $	Can. $	U.K. £
1	Coffee pot	Cream; green band; mauve flowers; black leaves	192	75.00	100.00	50.00

GREEN LEAVES WITH FLOWERS DESIGN

WINDSOR

Backstamp: Black ink stamp "Wadeheath England" with lion

No.	Description	Colourways	Size	U.S. $	Can. $	U.K. £
1	Coffee pot	Cream; green leaves; small blue flowers	192	75.00	100.00	50.00

UNKNOWN SHAPES

U
N
K
N
O
W
N

APPLE BLOSSOM DESIGN, c.1945

This design has one large blossom branch and two small sprigs of flowers.

For an illustration
of this design
see page 143

Backstamp: Green ink stamp "Wade England" (crossed W c.1945)

No.	Description	Colourways	Size	U.S. $	Can. $	U.K. £
1	Cup and saucer	White; pink/white blossoms; brown stems; yellow/green leaves	57/114	10.00	15.00	8.00

COPPER LEAVES, OAK LEAF AND BERRIES DESIGN, c.1953-1960

The design on this set was also used on other tablewares including Dandy jugs and sugar bowls.

Backstamp: Gold printed semi-circular "Wade Made in England Hand Painted" (c.1953-1960)

No.	Description	Colourways	Size	U.S. $	Can. $	U.K. £
1	Coffee pot	White; copper top/spout/handle/base/bands; white band with copper leaves and berries	180	50.00	70.00	35.00
2	Cup and saucer	White cup; copper bands, leaves and berries; white saucer; copper bands	57/114	12.00	15.00	8.00

FORSYTHIA DESIGN, 1937-c.1948

Backstamp: Black or green ink stamp "Wade Heath England" (round W 1937-c.1948)

No.	Description	Colourways	Size	U.S. $	Can. $	U.K. £
1	Coffee pot	Cream; gold rim; brown stems; grey leaves; yellow flowers	210	45.00	60.00	30.00
2	Cream jug		85	12.00	15.00	8.00
3	Cup and saucer		55/115	10.00	12.00	6.00
4	Sugar bowl		40	6.00	8.00	4.00

GOLD LEAF DESIGN

Backstamp: Black ink stamp "Wadeheath England" with lion (1934-1937)

No.	Description	Colourways	Size	U.S. $	Can. $	U.K. £
1	Coffee pot	White; gold striped lid and finial; gold foot and leaves	210	45.00	60.00	30.00

MOTTLED DESIGN, c.1945

UNKNOWN

Backstamp: Black ink stamp "Wade Heath England" with impressed "Made in England" (rounded W c.1945-c.1948)

No.	Description	Colourways	Size	U.S. $	Can. $	U.K. £
1	Coffee pot	Mottled yellow/green	195	65.00	90.00	45.00

DECANTERS, GOBLETS, JUGS, TANKARDS AND PITCHERS

This section is divided into two sub-sections. The first section covers decanters, jugs, goblets and tankards that would normally be used for alcoholic beverages. The second section includes table jugs and pitchers of the type commonly used for beverages such as milk and lemonade.

COPPER LUSTRE
By Wade of England

A group of sparkling tableware items with hand painted Cranberry design with red berries and green leaves on white background and heavy Copper Lustre borders. Available open stock or in suggested 10-pce. Package (58/130).

58/134
TEAPOT
3 Cup

58/138
COV'D. CANDY BOX 5'' x 4''.

58/132
CREAM &
SUGAR

58/133   TEAPOT
5 Cup

58/139
TRAY
RECTANGULAR 4¼'' x 3''

58/135 JUG
½ pt.

58/136 JUG
1 pt.

58/137 JUG
1½ pt.

58/131
CREAM &
SUGAR individual

9/613
COVERED CANDY BOXES

Decorated with old English prints and hand-filled in natural colors.

9/612
BON BON
Rectangle bon bons to match No. 9/613 candy boxes.

Cassidy's Ltd.

B 37

Decanters, Goblets, Jugs and Tankards

SHAPE NAME INDEX

DECANTERS

BOSUNS, 1993

This Bosuns decanter was part of an eight piece executive desk set produced by Wade Ceramics for specific companies to give as gifts to their business clients.

Photograph of this
design not available
at press time

Backstamp: Unknown

No.	Description	Colourways	Size	U.S. $	Can. $	U.K. £
1	Bosuns decanter	Black; gold edges and emblem	240	55.00	70.00	35.00

FALSTAFF, c. 1975

Wade produced the porcelain part of the decanter and the silver plated spouts, lids and handles were attached by Falstaff Silver Plating Co. of Birmingham. The spouts on the claret jugs are formed from the mask of a man's bearded face. See page ?? for sugar bowl.

ROYAL BLUE DESIGN

Backstamp: Embossed "Wade Falstaff England" with paper label "Falstaff Silver Plated Collection"

No.	Description	Colourways	Size	U.S. $	Can. $	U.K. £
1	Claret jug, large	Royal blue; silver plated lid/handle	295	90.00	120.00	60.00
2	Claret jug, small		196	65.00	90.00	45.00

WHITE WITH ROSES DESIGN

Backstamp: Embossed "Wade Falstaff England" with paper label "Falstaff Silver Plated Collection"

No.	Description	Colourways	Size	U.S. $	Can. $	U.K. £
1	Claret jug, large	White; red roses print; silver plated lid/handle	295	90.00	120.00	60.00
2	Claret jug, small		196	65.00	90.00	45.00

FLAGON, c.1953

Backstamp: Red printed "Wade England" (1953-c.1962)

No.	Description	Colourways	Size	U.S. $	Can. $	U.K. £
1	Flagon	Amber; copper band, handle, foot	165	55.00	70.00	35.00

FLAGON

IRISH WADE SHAPE No. I.P.60, 1982-1986

Backstamp: A. Black printed circular "Irish Porcelain Wade Ireland" with a shamrock and crown in the centre
Gold paper label in the shape of a "shamrock over a crown" glued onto the front of the jug
B. Embossed "Irish Porcelain Wade Made in Ireland" with a shamrock and crown in the centre

No.	Description	Colourways	Size	U.S. $	Can. $	U.K. £
1	Poteen jug/decanter	Grey/blue/greenish brown	205	55.00	70.00	35.00

IRISH WADE SHAPE No. S.R.13, 1982-1986

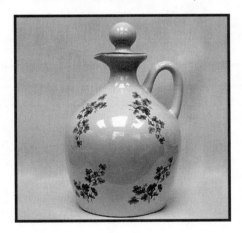

Backstamp: Green transfer printed "Made in Ireland Porcelain - Wade - eire tire a dheanta"

No.	Description	Colourways	Size	U.S. $	Can. $	U.K. £
1	Shamrock poteen decanter	White; green shamrocks	200	55.00	70.00	35.00

IRISH WADE SHAPE No. UNKNOWN, c.1970

Photograph of this
design not available
at press time

Backstamp: Black printed "Wade Ireland"

No.	Description	Colourways	Size	U.S. $	Can. $	U.K. £
1	Stoneware Irish poteen jug/decanter	Grey stone top; green bottom	175 x 130	25.00	35.00	20.00

IRISH WADE SHAPE No. UNKNOWN, c.1950

The dainty shaped decanter has an impressed decoration of bands and crosses, the six goblets have only the impressed bands.

Backstamp: A. Impressed "Irish Porcelain" curved over shamrock leaf "Made in Ireland" (c.1950)
B. Impressed "Irish Porcelain" curved over shamrock leaf "Made in Ireland by Wade Co. Armagh" (c.1950)

No.	Description	Colourways	Size	U.S. $	Can. $	U.K. £
1	Decanter	Green brown/ blue grey	225	65.00	90.00	45.00
2	Goblet		63	12.00	16.00	8.00

I
R
I
S
H

W
A
D
E

GOBLETS

ETCHED GOBLET

This small goblet has four lily/orchid type flowers etched around the surface.

E
T
C
H
E
D

Backstamp: Impressed "Irish Porcelain" (curved over shamrock) Made in Ireland" in straight line

No.	Description	Colourways	Size	U.S. $	Can. $	U.K. £
1	Etched goblet	Greeny brown	104	12.00	15.00	8.00

IRISH GOBLET, 1983 - 1986

These same transfer prints were used on Wade Ireland giftware bells (see *The Charlton Standard Catalogue of Wade Volume 2*).

Backstamp: Green printed "Made in Ireland Porcelain Wade eire tir A dheanta"
Colourway: White goblet; gold rings; multi-coloured print

No.	Description	Irish Wade Shape No.	Size	U.S. $	Can. $	U.K. £
1a	Blarney Castle	No. SR14/1	115	40.00	50.00	25.00
1b	Bunratty Castle	No. SR14/3	115	40.00	50.00	25.00
1c	Irish Harp	No. SR14	115	40.00	50.00	25.00
1d	Ross Castle	No. SR14/2	115	40.00	50.00	25.00
1e	Shamrocks	No. SR14/5	115	40.00	50.00	25.00
1f	Spinning Wheel	No. SR14/4	115	40.00	50.00	25.00
1g	Thatched Cottage	No. SR14/8	115	40.00	50.00	25.00

IRISH WADE SHAPE No. I.P. 7, c.1950 - c.1979

This beaker has one row of embossed shamrocks and four rows of impressed and embossed knurls.

Backstamp: Impressed "Irish Porcelain" (curved over large shamrock)
"Made in Ireland" in straight line (c. 1952-c.1955, c.1970)

No.	Description	Colourways	Size	U.S. $	Can. $	U.K. £
1	Knurled beaker	Blue green	98	12.00	15.00	8.00

ULSTER WARE GOBLETS

In early 1953 Wade (Ulster) Ltd. Co. Armagh produced a very limited range of coronation ware goblets in both round and straight-sided versions. The enameled decoration on the goblets was known as Coronation and the style which has designs of crossed bands and raised dots was known as Ulster Ware. The Ulster Ware raised dot shape goblet was produced a number of times during the next 30 years in the well known grey- blue/greeny-brown Irish glazes, but the coronation colours were never used again.

SHAPE NO I.P. 10A, 1953-c.1980

This round knurled goblet has two rows of knurls around the bowl and a row of embossed dots around the stem.

Backstamp: Impressed "Irish Porcelain Co. Armagh" with "Wade" inside a shamrock leaf

No.	Description	Colourways	Size	U.S. $	Can. $	U.K. £
1a	Round knurled goblet	Green-brown	140	30.00	40.00	20.00
1b	Round knurled goblet	Grey-blue	140	30.00	40.00	20.00

U L S T E R W A R E

SHAPE No. UNKNOWN

Version One — Crossed Bands

Photograph of this
design not available
at press time

Backstamp: Unmarked

No.	Description	Colourways	Size	U.S. $	Can. $	U.K. £
1	Goblet	Emerald green	120	60.00	80.00	40.00

Version Two — Raised Dots

Backstamp: Unmarked

No.	Description	Colourways	Size	U.S. $	Can. $	U.K. £
1a	Goblet	Brown/green	120	30.00	40.00	20.00
1b	Goblet	Pastel blue	120	60.00	80.00	40.00
1c	Goblet	Pink/fawn	120	60.00	80.00	40.00
1d	Goblet	Purple/lilac/emerald green	120	60.00	80.00	40.00

ULSTER WARE

JUGS AND TANKARDS

GALLEON JUG AND TANKARD SET, 1934-1937

This unusually shaped jug was produced with six matching tankards. They were designed by Georgina Lawton.

Backstamp: A. Red ink stamp "Wadeheath England" with lion and handpainted "No 3504p" (c.1933-1934) (Jugs)
B. Black ink stamp "Wadeheath Ware England" (c.1934-1937) (Tankards)

No.	Description	Colourways	Size	U.S. $	Can. $	U.K. £
1a	Galleon jug	Cream; bright orange sails; light brown galleon; grey blue waves	205	170.00	230.00	115.00
1b	Galleon jug	Cream; orange/ red sails; purple/mauve galleon; pale blue waves	205	170.00	230.00	115.00
1c	Galleon jug	Cream; green sails; dark brown galleon; grey blue waves	205	170.00	230.00	115.00
1d	Galleon jug	Mottled green	205	140.00	190.00	95.00
2a	Galleon tankard	Cream; bright orange sails; light brown galleon; grey blue waves	110	45.00	60.00	30.00
2b	Galleon tankard	Cream; orange/red sails; purple/ mauve galleon; pale blue waves	110	45.00	60.00	30.00
2c	Galleon tankard	Cream; green sails; dark brown galleon; grey blue waves	110	45.00	60.00	30.00
2d	Galleon tankard	Mottled green	110	40.00	50.00	25.00

G
A
L
L
E
O
N

LAMBETH WALK JUG & TANKARD SET, c.1938-1953

This jug was produced in both a musical and non-musical version. Both jugs have embossed designs of a man and woman dancing the Lambeth Walk on the front, a still popular Cockney song and dance which was sung in the British musical comedy *Me and My Girl* by Lupino Lane. On the back is an embossed organ grinder with monkey. The jug was produced with four matching tankards. On the front of the tankards is an embossed design of a man walking with his dog, and on the back is the word "Oi!," which is part of the song. The musical jug plays *The Lambeth Walk*.

L
A
M
B
E
T
H

W
A
L
K

Backstamp A. Ink stamp "Wade Heath England" (rounded W 1937-1940)
B. Ink stamp "Wade England" (crossed W c.1948-1953)

No.	Description	Colourways	Size	U.S. $	Can. $	U.K. £
1a	Musical jug	Honey brown; dark brown/green figures	270	300.00	400.00	200.00
1b	Non-musical jug	Honey brown; dark brown/green figures	270	225.00	300.00	150.00
2	Tankards	Honey brown; dark brown figure/dog	120	55.00	70.00	35.00

BEER MUGS, c.1948-1953

These tankards are the same shape as used for the Cranky Tankards series (see *The Charlton Standard Catalogue of Wade, Volume 2*).

BANDED DESIGN

Backstamp: Green ink stamp "Harvest Ware Wade England"

No.	Description	Colourways	Size	U.S. $	Can. $	U.K. £
1	Tankard	Cream; red/mauve/yellow/black bands; black base	122	25.00	35.00	18.00

GEORGIAN OAK DESIGN

Backstamp: Green ink stamp "Harvest Ware Wade England"

No.	Description	Colourways	Size	U.S. $	Can. $	U.K. £
1	Tankard	Copper; white acorns/leaves	122	35.00	50.00	25.00

PEONIES DESIGN

B
E
E
R

M
U
G
S

Backstamp: Green ink stamp "Harvest Ware Wade England"

No.	Description	Colourways	Size	U.S. $	Can. $	U.K. £
1	Tankard	Copper rim, handle/base; cream tankard; purple/yellow flower; brown streaks; green leaves	122	35.00	50.00	25.00

VINE AND BERRIES DESIGN

Variation 1 — Two copper leaves and berries

For an illustration
of this design
see page 43

Backstamp: Green ink stamp "Harvest Ware Wade England"

No.	Description	Colourways	Size	U.S. $	Can. $	U.K. £
1	Tankard	Copper rim/handle/base; blue tankard; copper vine, leaves, berries	122	35.00	50.00	25.00

Variation 2 — Three serrated leaves and berries

Backstamp: Green ink stamp "Harvest Ware Wade England"

No.	Description	Colourways	Size	U.S. $	Can. $	U.K. £
1	Tankard	Copper rim/handle/base; cream tankard; dark green vine, leaves, berries	122	35.00	50.00	25.00

MOURNE TANKARDS, 1971-1976

The lovely mourne glazes were only used on fifteen items in the Mourne series produced between 1971-1976. Completely unlike the normal Irish Wade glazes, these tankards are in mellowed greens, browns and orange with etched designs of flowers on both sides (for Mourne vases see *The Charlton Standard Catalogue of Wade, Volume 2*).

Backstamp: Unknown

No.	Description	Colourways	Size	U.S. $	Can. $	U.K. £
1	Tankard, pint (C.352)	Green brown; orange flowers	127	60.00	80.00	40.00
2	Tankard, ½ pint (C.351)		101	55.00	70.00	35.00

OVAL PANEL TANKARDS, 1992

These tankards have an embossed oval panel on the front which on the "Jacobean" floral design tankard is obscured by the print.

Backstamp: Red printed "Wade England" with two lines

No.	Description	Colourways	Size	U.S. $	Can. $	U.K. £
1a	"Dad" tankard	Cream; gold base rim; black lettering	110	20.00	25.00	12.00
1b	Jacobean tankard	Cream; orange/ black floral print	110	30.00	40.00	20.00

SHAMROCK RANGE TANKARDS, 1983-1986

Wade Ireland produced two tankards during this three year period. Both are white with the green shamrock decoration. The half pint tankard is in the traditional English tankard shape and the pint tankard is in the Irish knurled tankard shape with two rows of knurls around the base.

STYLE ONE — SR1

For an illustration
of this design
see page 142

Backstamp: Unknown

No.	Description	Colourways	Size	U.S. $	Can. $	U.K. £
1	Tankard, ½ pint	White; gold bands; green shamrock	105	20.00	25.00	12.00

STYLE TWO — SR2

For an illustration
of this design
see page 142

Backstamp: Unknown

No.	Description	Colourways	Size	U.S. $	Can. $	U.K. £
1	Tankard, pint	White; gold bands; green shamrock	155	20.00	25.00	12.00

Pitchers and Table Jugs

Wadeheath produced jugs and pitchers in various shapes and a number of sizes which were intended for use as milk jugs. The largest jug could hold one and half pints. Some jugs were given a shape name by Wadeheath, others have only a design name or a number. Wadeheath advertising often referred to jugs as 24s, 30s, 36s and 42s. This did not refer directly to the actual size of the product, but to the number of jugs that could be packed into a standard size shipping container.

SHAPE NAME INDEX

BEE SHAPE, 1932-1950

For other Bee shape items, see pages 14 and 201.

Backstamp: Orange ink stamp "Wades England" with lion (1927-1933)

No.	Description	Colourways	Size	U.S. $	Can. $	U.K. £
1a	Milk jug	Cream; gold highlighting; orange and white flowers; pale blue leaves	175	50.00	65.00	30.00
1b	Milk jug	Cream; multi-coloured flowers; green leaves	175	50.00	65.00	30.00
1c	Milk jug	Cream; white heron multi-coloured flowers	175	50.00	65.00	30.00

CLASSIC KINGS SHAPE, 1993

For other items in this shape see pages 331, 336, 337, 343, 349, 429.

For an illustration
of this design
see page 328

Backstamp: Printed "Wade" between two lines

No.	Description	Colourways	Size	U.S. $	Can. $	U.K. £
1a	Milk jug	Cream	114	18.00	25.00	12.00
1b	Milk jug	Dark green; gold edging	114	18.00	25.00	12.00
1c	Milk jug	White	114	18.00	25.00	12.00
1d	Milk jug	White; gold edging	114	18.00	25.00	12.00

B
E
E

DIAMOND SHAPE, c.1948-1961

BARLEY AND COPPER LUSTRE DESIGN

Photograph of this
design not available
at press time

Backstamp: Gold printed semi-circular "Wade made in England Hand Painted"

No.	Description	Colourways	Size	U.S. $	Can. $	U.K. £
1	Milk jug, extra large	Copper; yellow barley ears	230	50.00	65.00	35.00

CLOVER AND COPPER LUSTRE DESIGN

Photograph of this
design not available
at press time

Backstamp: **A.** Green or black ink stamp "Wade England" (crossed W c.1948-c.1953)
B. Gold printed semi-circular "Wade made in England Hand Painted"

No.	Description	Colourways	Size	U.S. $	Can. $	U.K. £
1	Milk jug, large	Copper; pink/yellow/green clover and leaves	150	35.00	45.00	25.00
2	Milk jug, medium	Copper; hand-painted clover and flowers	127	35.00	45.00	25.00

COPPER LUSTRE DESIGN

Backstamp: **A.** Green or black ink stamp "Wade England" (crossed W c.1948-c.1953)
B. Green printed "Wade England"
C. Gold printed semi-circular "Wade made in England Hand Painted"

No.	Description	Colourways	Size	U.S. $	Can. $	U.K. £
1	Milk jug, large	Copper lustre	150	25.00	35.00	18.00
2	Milk jug, medium		127	25.00	35.00	18.00

DIAMOND

FLORAL AND COPPER LUSTRE DESIGN

Photograph of this
design not available
at press time

Backstamp: Gold printed semi-circular "Wade made in England Hand Painted" (1953-1960)

No.	Description	Colourways	Size	U.S. $	Can. $	U.K. £
1	Milk jug, medium	Copper; pink flower; green leaves	127	35.00	45.00	25.00

GEORGIAN OAK AND COPPER LUSTRE DESIGN

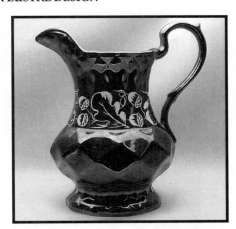

Backstamp: Green or black ink stamp "Wade England" (crossed W c.1948-c.1953)

No.	Description	Colourways	Size	U.S. $	Can. $	U.K. £
1	Milk jug, large	Copper; white oak leaves and acorns	150	35.00	45.00	25.00

SILVER LUSTRE DESIGN

Photograph of this
design not available
at press time

Backstamp: **A.** Green or black ink stamp "Wade England" (crossed W c.1948-c.1953)
B. Green printed "Wade England"

No.	Description	Colourways	Size	U.S. $	Can. $	U.K. £
1	Milk jug, medium	Silver lustre	127	40.00	55.00	28.00
2	Milk jug, small		114	40.00	50.00	28.00

DIAMOND

DUTCH SHAPE, c.1932 - 1953

A 1932 Wadeheath advertisement shows a Dutch milk jug with the name Toby. In the mid-1930s, because of confusion with the name Toby and a Wade Toby Jug which is a jug shaped as a man, the name was changed to Dutch jug. These jugs were produced in small, medium, large and extra large sizes.

ASTER DESIGN

For an illustration
of this design
see page 362

Backstamp: Gold printed semi-circular "Wade Made in England Hand painted" (1953-1960)

No.	Description	Colourways	Size	U.S. $	Can. $	U.K. £
1	Jug, medium	Copper; pink flower; green leaves	114	55.00	70.00	35.00

ASTER AND PEONIES DESIGN

Backstamp: Black ink stamp "Wade Heath England" (round W 1937-1940)

No.	Description	Colourways	Size	U.S. $	Can. $	U.K. £
1	Jug, extra large	Copper neck/ handle/base; maroon/mauve flowers; green leaves	133	55.00	70.00	40.00

CLOVER DESIGN

For an illustration
of this design
see page 363

Backstamp: Green ink stamp "Harvest Ware Wade England" (c.1948-1953)

No.	Description	Colourways	Size	U.S. $	Can. $	U.K. £
1	Jug, small	Copper; pink/yellow/green clover and leaves	101	40.00	50.00	25.00

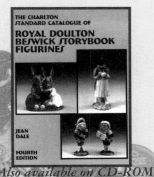

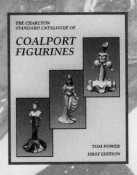
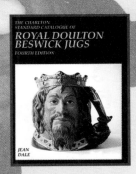

COPPER LEAVES DESIGN

Backstamp: Black ink stamp "Wade Heath England" (round W 1937-1940)

No.	Description	Colourways	Size	U.S. $	Can. $	U.K. £
1	Jug, medium	Cream; copper neck/handle/base copper leaves	114	55.00	70.00	35.00

DAISIES DESIGN

Variation 1 — Heart-shaped petals

Backstamp: Green ink stamp "Harvest Ware Wade England" (c.1948-1953)

No.	Description	Colourways	Size	U.S. $	Can. $	U.K. £
1	Jug, large	Cream; mauve/purple flowers; green leaves/bands; brown streaks	127	55.00	70.00	40.00
2	Jug, medium	Copper neck/handle/base; mauve/purple flowers; green leaves; brown streaks	114	55.00	70.00	35.00

Variation 2 — Pointed petals

Backstamp: Black ink stamp "Wade Heath England" (round W 1937-1940)

No.	Description	Colourways	Size	U.S. $	Can. $	U.K. £
1a	Jug, medium	Cream; maroon/blue flowers; green/brown leaves; green bands	114	55.00	70.00	35.00
1b	Jug, medium	Copper neck/handle/base; maroon/blue flowers; green/ brown leaves	114	55.00	70.00	35.00
2	Jug, small		101	40.00	50.00	25.00

Variation 3 — Round petals

Backstamp: Black ink stamp "Wade Heath England" (round W 1937-1940)

No.	Description	Colourways	Size	U.S. $	Can. $	U.K. £
1	Jug, medium	Copper neck/shoulder/handle/base; maroon/ purple flowers; green/brown leaves	114	55.00	70.00	35.00

DUTCH

HONEYSUCKLE DESIGN

Backstamp: A. Black ink stamp "Wade Heath England" (round W 1937-1940)
           B. Green ink stamp "Harvest Ware Wade England" (c.1948-1953)

No.	Description	Colourways	Size	U.S. $	Can. $	U.K. £
1	Jug, extra large	Copper neck/handle/base; purple/ maroon flowers; green/orange leaves	133	55.00	70.00	40.00

MULBERRY DESIGN

The outline design of leaves and berries resemble mulberry leaves.

Photograph of this
design not available
at press time

Backstamp: Black ink stamp "Wade Heath England" (round W 1937-1940)

No.	Description	Colourways	Size	U.S. $	Can. $	U.K. £
1	Jug, large	Copper; white leaves and berries	127	55.00	70.00	40.00

PEONIES DESIGN

One of Wades most used designs is the hand-painted peony flowers which are found on many of Wades decorative vases and jugs.

Backstamp: Green ink stamp "Harvest Ware Wade England" (c.1948-1953)

No.	Description	Colourways	Size	U.S. $	Can. $	U.K. £
1	Jug, large	Copper neck/handle/base; purple/yellow; maroon/yellow flowers; green/brown leaves	127	55.00	70.00	40.00

PLUMS DESIGN

This design of purple and maroon plums was also used on the Dandy jugs.

Backstamp: Green ink stamp "Harvest Ware Wade England" (c.1948-1953)

No.	Description	Colourways	Size	U.S. $	Can. $	U.K. £
1	Jug, medium	Copper neck/handle/base; purple/maroon plums; green/yellow green leaves	114	55.00	70.00	35.00

DUTCH

POPPY DESIGN

This hand-painted design is of open poppy flowers with the poppy seed pod in the centre.

For an illustration
of this design
see page 215

Backstamp: Black ink stamp "Wade Heath England" (round W 1937-1940)

No.	Description	Colourways	Size	U.S. $	Can. $	U.K. £
1	Jug, large	Cream; light brown band on neck; maroon/mauve flowers; green/brown leaves	127	55.00	70.00	40.00
2	Jug, small	Copper neck/handle/base; maroon/mauve flowers; green/brown leaves	101	40.00	50.00	25.00

ROSE DESIGN

Backstamp: Black ink stamp "Wade Heath England" (round W 1937-1940)

No.	Description	Colourways	Size	U.S. $	Can. $	U.K. £
1	Jug, small	Copper; dark green band; pink rose; green leaves	101	40.00	50.00	25.00

VINE AND BERRIES DESIGN

Variation 1 —Three serrated leaves and berries

For an illustration
of this design
see page 44

Backstamp: Green ink stamp "Harvest Ware Wade England"

No.	Description	Colourways	Size	U.S. $	Can. $	U.K. £
1	Jug, large	Copper neck/handle/base; dark green leaves/berries	127	55.00	70.00	40.00

Variation 2 — *Five large pointed leaves and berries*

Photograph of this
design not available
at press time

Backstamp: Black ink stamp "Wade Heath England" (round W 1937-1940)

No.	Description	Colourways	Size	U.S. $	Can. $	U.K. £
1	Jug, medium	Copper neck/handle/base; green/yellow brown leaves; red berries	114	55.00	70.00	35.00

Variation 3 — *Large serrated leaves and berries*

Backstamp: Green ink stamp "Harvest Ware Wade England"

No.	Description	Colourways	Size	U.S. $	Can. $	U.K. £
1	Jug, large	Copper neck/handle/base; green/yellow vine leaves; red berries	127	55.00	70.00	40.00

WHEAT EARS DESIGN

Photograph of this
design not available
at press time

Backstamp: Green ink stamp "Wade England" (crossed W 1940)

No.	Description	Colourways	Size	U.S. $	Can. $	U.K. £
1	Jug, medium	Copper; yellow wheat; green leaves	114	55.00	70.00	35.00

D
U
T
C
H

ETON SHAPE, 1937-1940

MARIGOLD FLOWERS AND TREE DESIGN

Backstamp: **A.** Black ink stamp "Wadeheath England" with lion (1933-1937)
B. Green ink stamp "Wade Heath England" (round W 1937-1940)

No.	Description	Colourways	Size	U.S. $	Can. $	U.K. £
1	Jug, large	White; green/yellow tree leaves; brown trunk; orange flowers; green grass	159	45.00	55.00	28.00
2	Jug, medium	White; black/green tree leaves; brown trunk; orange flowers; green grass	153	45.00	55.00	28.00
3	Jug, small	White; black/green/yellow tree leaves brown trunk; orange flowers; green grass	140	45.00	55.00	28.00

LATTICE SHAPE, c.1940 - c.1968

Although these milk jugs have the same design name as the Lattice Tea Set (see page 80) the embossed diamond shaped lattice design is only around the bottom of the jug and there are different hand-painted designs on the top half.

CLOVER DESIGN

Backstamp: Ink stamp "Wade England"

No.	Description	Colourways	Size	U.S. $	Can. $	U.K. £
1	Jug, large	Copper lustre; pink/yellow/green clover and leaves	153	55.00	70.00	35.00
2	Jug, medium		127	50.00	60.00	30.00
3	Jug, small		114	50.00	60.00	30.00

COPPER LUSTRE DESIGN

Photograph of this
design not available
at press time

Backstamp: Ink stamp "Wade England"

No.	Description	Colourways	Size	U.S. $	Can. $	U.K. £
1	Jug, large	Copper lustre	153	40.00	45.00	25.00
2	Jug, medium		127	35.00	40.00	20.00
3	Jug, small		114	35.00	40.00	20.00

COTONEASTER BERRIES DESIGN

Backstamp: Gold printed semi-circular "Wade Made in England Hand Painted"

No.	Description	Colourways	Size	U.S. $	Can. $	U.K. £
1	Jug, medium	Copper; yellow berries; green leaves	127	50.00	60.00	30.00
2	Jug, small		114	50.00	60.00	30.00

PEKIN SHAPE, 1930

JEWEL DESIGN

For teapots in this shape see page 216.

Backstamp: Orange ink stamp "Wades England" with lion (1927-1933)

No.	Description	Colourways	Size	U.S. $	Can. $	U.K. £
1	Milk jug	Black jug; gold lines; gold/orange/blue jewels	155	45.00	60.00	30.00

POLKA SHAPE, c. 1938-c.1942

Polka was so named because of the embossed folk dancers on the jug. In some cases the design is difficult to see because of the heavy copper lustre glazing. In 1951 the jug was reissued, this time in new multiple colours with copper lustre highlights and was renamed Festival (see page 55).

P
O
L
K
A

Backstamp: **A.** Black ink stamp "Made in England" (c.1938-c.1942)
B. Green or black ink stamp "Wade England" (c.1948-1953)

No.	Description	Colourways	Size	U.S. $	Can. $	U.K. £
1	Jug, medium	Copper lustre	146	45.00	55.00	30.00
2	Jug, small		127	40.00	50.00	25.00

ROSS SHAPE, c.1933-1937

BOXES AND FLOWERS DESIGN

Photograph of this
design not available
at press time

Backstamp: Black ink stamp "Wadeheath England" with lion (1934-1937)

No.	Description	Colourways	Size	U.S. $	Can. $	U.K. £
1	Jug, large	Cream; black/cream/orange squares; large orange flowers; green leaves	127	50.00	40.00	20.00

FLOWERS DESIGN

Backstamp: Red ink stamp "Wadeheath England" with lion, embossed "98 Ross" (1933)

No.	Description	Colourways	Size	U.S. $	Can. $	U.K. £
1a	Jug, extra large	Cream; blue/brown flower; orange/brown flower; green leaves	135	30.00	40.00	20.00
1b	Jug, extra large	Cream; purple/green flower; orange/blue flower; orange/yellow/black flower	135	30.00	40.00	20.00
2	Jug, small	Cream; orange/green flower; yellow/black flower; purple/yellow flower	114	30.00	40.00	20.00

SPIDER WEB DESIGN

Backstamp: Black ink stamp "Wadeheath England" with lion (1934-1937)

No.	Description	Colourways	Size	U.S. $	Can. $	U.K. £
1	Jug, extra large	Cream; brown tree; orange flowers; black web	135	55.00	45.00	25.00
2	Jug, large		127	55.00	45.00	25.00
3	Jug, medium		120	55.00	45.00	25.00

STREAKED DESIGN

Backstamp: Black ink stamp "Wadeheath England" with lion (1933-1934)

No.	Description	Colourways	Size	U.S. $	Can. $	U.K. £
1	Jug, large	Pink/turquoise streaks	127	50.00	40.00	20.00

SELBY SHAPE, 1930

For additional patterns in this shape see pages 139 and 224-225.

GARLANDS DESIGN

Backstamp: Orange ink stamp " Wades England with lion" (1927-1933)

No.	Description	Colourways	Size	U.S. $	Can. $	U.K. £
1	Milk jug	White; gold bands, garland decoration; multi-coloured flowers prints	unknown	75.00	100.00	50.00

STAG SHAPE, c.1948 - c.1960

These jugs have an embossed design of stags and does. On some of the pieces the design is barely visible because of the thick glaze. For bowls in this shape see page 378.

Backstamp: Red printed "Wade England" (1953-c.1962)

No.	Description	Colourways	Size	U.S. $	Can. $	U.K. £
1	Milk jug, extra large	Copper lustre	171	55.00	70.00	35.00
2	Milk jug, large		159	55.00	70.00	35.00
3	Milk jug, medium		146	45.00	55.00	30.00
4	Milk jug, small		133	40.00	50.00	25.00

UNKNOWN SHAPES

Only a design name can be given for the following jugs until more information is discovered.

BLACK WITH GOLD DESIGN

Backstamp: Red ink stamp " Wadeheath England" with lion (1934-1937)

No.	Description	Colourways	Size	U.S. $	Can. $	U.K. £
1	Jug	Black; gold bands and highlighting	135	30.00	40.00	20.00

EMBOSSED BANDS DESIGN, c.1945

Backstamp: Green ink stamp " Wade Heath England" (straight W c.1945-c.1952)

No.	Description	Colourways	Size	U.S. $	Can. $	U.K. £
1a	Jug	White; yellow/orange/grey balls; black stem; yellow/green leaves	135	30.00	40.00	20.00
1b	Jug	White; yellow/orange flowers; black stem; yellow/green leaves	135	30.00	40.00	20.00

FRUIT TREES AND HOUSES DESIGN, 1934-1937

UNKNOWN

Backstamp: Black ink stamp " Wadeheath England" with lion (1934-1937)

No.	Description	Colourways	Size	U.S. $	Can. $	U.K. £
1	Milk jug	White; yellow/orange/mauve fruits; black trees; green leaves; yellow/orange/ mauve houses	153	40.00	60.00	30.00

SUNRISE DESIGN

Backstamp: Black ink stamp "Wadeheath England" with lion (1934-1937)

No.	Description	Colourways	Size	U.S. $	Can. $	U.K. £
1	Milk jug	White; orange/yellow/grey flowers; black tree; green leaves; orange/yellow sunrise	153	55.00	70.00	35.00

TABLEWARE

Classic Kings/Kings

Tableware Accouterments

This section contains those items which would be used during a meal, such as butter dishes, cheese dishes, cruets, egg cups, mustard pots, preserve pots and salt and pepper.

SHAPE NAME INDEX

Butter Dishes

Cheese Dishes

Cruets

Egg Coddlers and Egg Cups

Honey and Preserve Jars

BUTTER DISHES

CLASSIC KINGS/KINGS SHAPE, 1992-1993

The items in this set have an embossed leaf design and were originally produced in white or cream with the name "Kings Kitchenware." In late 1993 two new colours, dark green with gold edging and white with gold edging were added and the name was then changed to Classic Kings Kitchenware. For other Classic Kings pieces see pages 307, 328, 336, 337, 343, 349, 397 and 429.

Backstamp: Printed "Wade England" with two lines

No.	Description	Colourways	Size	U.S.$	Can. $	U.K. £
1a	Butter dish	Cream	101	12.00	15.00	8.00
1b	Butter dish	Dark green; gold edging	101	15.00	20.00	10.00
1c	Butter dish	White	101	12.00	15.00	8.00
1d	Butter dish	White; gold edging	101	15.00	20.00	10.00

IRISH WADE SHAPE NO. I.P.75, c.1950 - c.1975

This butter dish is saucer shaped and can be found with a number of different transfer prints.

Backstamp: **A.** Ink stamp " Irish Porcelain Wade Co Armagh Made in Ireland"
B. Ink stamp "Irish Porcelain" slanted over a shamrock leaf with "Wade Co. Armagh" in a straight line (c.1955)
C. Impressed "Made in Ireland by Wade" (c.1975)

No.	Description	Colourways	Size	U.S. $	Can. $	U.K. £
1a	Finn McCaul	Browny green; multi-coloured print	127	15.00	20.00	10.00
1b	Fox hunter hat on head		127	15.00	20.00	10.00
1c	Fox hunter hat in hand		127	15.00	20.00	10.00
1d	Irish Jaunting Car		127	15.00	20.00	10.00
1e	Passenger Coach		127	15.00	20.00	10.00

IRISH WADE SHAPE NO I.P. 619, c.1955-c.1985

The Irish Wade butter pat dishes were also used, minus the transfer prints, as the base for the lucky leprechaun pintrays.

Backstamp: A. Embossed circular "Irish Porcelain Made in Ireland" around a central shamrock with a letter
B. Impressed "Made in Ireland by Wade" (c. 1978)
C. Embossed "Made in Ireland Irish Porcelain" with a centre shamrock and crown "Wade eire tir A dheanta"

No.	Description	Colourways	Size	U.S. $	Can. $	U.K. £
1a	Duck hunter standing	Browny green; multi-coloured print	127	6.00	10.00	5.00
1b	Fox hunter hat in hand		127	6.00	10.00	5.00
1c	Finn McCaul		127	6.00	10.00	5.00
1d	Flying ducks		127	6.00	10.00	5.00
1e	Galleon	Browny green; green print	127	6.00	10.00	5.00
1f	Irish colleen	Browny green; multi-coloured print	127	6.00	10.00	5.00
1g	Irish jaunting car		127	6.00	10.00	5.00
1h	Irish passenger coach		127	6.00	10.00	5.00
1i	No print	Browny green	127	3.00	8.00	4.00
1j	Stags head	Browny green; multi-coloured print	127	6.00	10.00	5.00

I
R
I
S
H

W
A
D
E

VILLAGE STORES SERIES, 1982-1986

The original price for the Village Store Post Office butter dish was £8.50. For the matching cheese dish see page 326, for the salt and pepper set see page 340, and for the matching storage containers see page 399.

V I L L A G E S T O R E S

Backstamp: Black printed "Village Stores by Wade Staffordshire England"

No.	Description	Colourways	Size	U.S. $	Can. $	U.K. £
1	Butter dish	White; pale yellow roof; multi-coloured print; black lettering	125	60.00	80.00	40.00

UNKNOWN SHAPES

ANIMAL PRINTS DESIGN, c.1985

These wedge shaped butter dishes have transfer prints of a fawn or a red squirrel on the cover.

Backstamp: Printed semi-circular "Royal Victoria Pottery Staffordshire Wade England"

No.	Description	Colourways	Size	U.S. $	Can. $	U.K. £
1a	Fawn butter dish	White; green edging; green/brown print	90	30.00	40.00	20.00
1b	Squirrel butter dish	White; green edging; green/yellow/brown print	90	30.00	40.00	20.00

FLOWERS DESIGN, 1927-1933

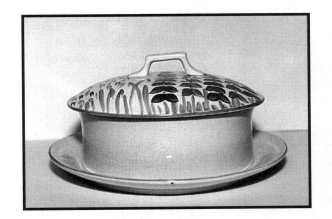

Backstamp: Ink stamp "Wade England" with lion

No.	Description	Colourways	Size	U.S. $	Can. $	U.K. £
1	Butter dish	Cream; pink/blue flowers; green grass/leaves	88 x 177	30.00	40.00	20.00

LEAVES DESIGN, 1927-1933

For an illustration
of this design
see page 14

Backstamp: Ink stamp "Wade England" with lion

No.	Description	Colourways	Size	U.S. $	Can. $	U.K. £
1	Butter dish	Cream; large orange leaves; grey flowers	88 x 177	30.00	40.00	20.00

CHEESE DISHES

CLASSIC KINGS/KINGS SHAPE, 1992-1993

The items in this set have an embossed leaf design and were originally produced in white or cream with the name "Kings Kitchenware. In late 1993 two new colours, dark green with gold edging and white with gold edging were added and the name was then changed to Classic Kings Kitchenware. For accompanying pieces please see pages 307, 331, 337, 343, 349 and 429.

For an illustration
of this shape
see page 328

Backstamp: Printed "Wade England" with two lines

No.	Description	Colourways	Size	U.S.$	Can. $	U.K. £
1a	Cheese dish	Cream	114	15.00	20.00	10.00
1b	Cheese dish	Dark green; gold edging	114	18.00	25.00	12.00
1c	Cheese dish	White	114	15.00	20.00	10.00
1d	Cheese dish	White; gold edging	114	18.00	25.00	12.00

VILLAGE STORES SERIES, 1982-1986

This cheese dish is backstamped inside the lid. The original price was £11.99. For the matching butter dish see page 334, for the salt and pepper set see page 340, and for the matching storage containers see page 399.

Backstamp: Black printed "Village Stores by Wade Staffordshire England"

No.	Description	Colourways	Size	U.S. $	Can. $	U.K. £
1	Cheese dish	Yellow roof; white dish; multi-coloured print; black lettering "The Chalk and Cheese"	150	70.00	95.00	45.00

CRUETS

CLASSIC KINGS/KINGS SHAPE, 1992-1993

The items in this set have an embossed leaf design and were originally produced in white or cream with the name "Kings Kitchenware. In late 1993 a new colourway, white with gold edging, was added and the name was changed to Classic Kings Kitchenware. For matching pieces see pages 307, 331, 336, 343, 349, 429.

For an illustration
of this shape
see page 328

Backstamp: Printed "Wade England" with two lines

No.	Description	Colourways	Size	U.S. $	Can. $	U.K. £
1a	Pepper pot	Cream	95	4.00	5.00	3.00
2a	Salt pot		95	4.00	5.00	3.00
1b	Pepper pot	White	95	4.00	5.00	3.00
2b	Salt pot		95	4.00	5.00	3.00
1c	Pepper pot	White; gold edging	95	4.00	5.00	3.00
2c	Salt pot		95	4.00	5.00	3.00

COUNTRYWARE, c.1975-1984

This cruet set in an amber brown glaze was produced at the Wade Ireland Pottery, Portadown, Northern Ireland. For matching storage containers see page 397, and for matching casserole dishes see page 409.

Backstamp: Impressed circular "Design Wade Country Ware Made in Ireland"

No.	Description	Irish Wade No.	Colourways	Size	U.S. $	Can. $	U.K. £
1	Mustard pot	KD 6	Amber	63	4.00	5.00	3.00
2	Pepper	KD 5		88	3.00	4.00	2.00
3	Pepper mill	KD 7		88	8.00	10.00	5.00
4	Salt	KD 4		88	3.00	4.00	2.00

IRISH WADE KNURLED SHAPE, c.1965 - c.1975

The knurled design is of two rows of knurls on the cruet and two rows of knurls and dots on the vinegar bottle. The pepper and salt pots were available as single items or as a cruet with a mustard pot on a shamrock shaped tray.

Cruet

Vinegar Bottle

Backstamp: Unknown

No.	Description	Irish Wade No.	Colourways	Size	U.S. $	Can. $	U.K. £
1	Cruet	I.P.606c	Green/ brown/ blue grey	76/113	38.00	50.00	25.00
2	Pepper pot	I.P.604		65	6.00	8.00	4.00
3	Salt pot	I.P.605		65	6.00	8.00	4.00
4	Vinegar bottle	I.P.111		171	38.00	50.00	25.00

TREE LOG SHAPE, 1954

This cruet was produced at the same time as the barbecue tankard (see *The Charlton Standard Catalogue of Wade Volume One General Issues*) and the log posy bowls (see *The Charlton Standard Catalogue of Wade Volume Two Decorative Wares*). It could be purchased gift boxed as a set of three or as a pair in a chrome stand. Each piece is identical in shape and size with the chrome lids being the only difference.

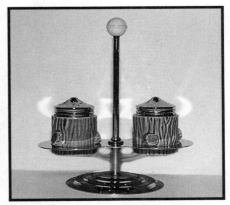

Backstamp: Impressed "R97/1"

No.	Description	Colourways	Size	U.S. $	Can. $	U.K. £
1a	Cruet (Boxed)	Beige	53	15.00	25.00	10.00
1b	Cruet (Boxed)	Green	53	15.00	25.00	10.00
2a	Salt/pepper on chrome stand	Beige	unknown	18.00	25.00	12.00
2b	Salt/pepper on chrome stand	Green	unknown	18.00	25.00	12.00

VILLAGE STORES SERIES, 1982-1986

For additional pieces in this series see pages 336 and 399.

GREENGROCER AND FAMILY BUTCHER DESIGN

Backstamp: Black printed "Village Stores by Wade Staffordshire England"

No.	Description	Colourways	Size	U.S. $	Can. $	U.K. £
1	A. Salt Prop. Greengrocer	Orange brown tile roof; white pot; multi-coloured print; black lettering	70	25.00	30.00	15.00
2	B. Pepper Family Butcher	Yellow brown tile roof; white pot; multi-coloured print; black lettering	70	25.00	30.00	15.00

POST OFFICE DESIGN

Though both pieces depict a country post office, the transfer designs are different. The salt pot has a pointed door and the pepper pot has a rounded door.

Photograph not
available at
press time

Backstamp: Black printed "Wade England"

No.	Description	Colourways	Size	U.S. $	Can. $	U.K. £
1	Post Office salt	Grey tile roof; white pot; multi-coloured print; pointed door; black lettering	53	20.00	25.00	10.00
2	Post Office Royal Mail pepper	Grey tile roof; white pot; multi-coloured print; rounded door; black lettering	53	20.00	25.00	10.00

EGG CODDLERS AND EGG CUPS

Only a very small number of egg cups were produced in the Wade Heath Pottery, most of the egg cups and egg coddlers were produced in the Wade Ireland Pottery.

EGG CODDLERS

IRISH WADE, c.1955-c.1975

The egg coddlers produced by Wade Ireland came in a single size (Shape No. I.P.631) and a double size (I.P.632). The screw on lids have a loop finial for easy removal from the saucepan. Some coddlers were produced as a special order for a Caribbean company and have an "A S Cooper" backstamp.

Backstamp: A. Embossed curved "Irish Porcelain" over straight "Made in Ireland"
B. Black ink stamp circular "Made in A S Cooper Ireland"

No.	Description	Colourways	Size	U.S. $	Can. $	U.K. £
1	Double coddler	Blue grey green	101	15.00	20.00	10.00
2a	Single coddler	Blue grey green	70	12.00	15.00	8.00
2b	Single coddler	Russet brown	70	12.00	15.00	8.00
2c	Single coddler	Blue grey green; black lettering "Solomon's Mines-Bahamas"	70	15.00	20.00	10.00

EGG CUPS

Egg Cups on Curved Edge Circular Tray, c.1900-1927

The semi-circular tray has four indentations for the egg cups.

C U R V E D E D G E

Backstamp: Red ink stamp "Wades England" (c.1900-1927)

No.	Description	Colourways	Size	U.S. $	Can. $	U.K. £
1	Egg cup/tray	Cream; grey/black flower; orange leaves	44/153	50.00	70.00	35.00

Egg Cups on Square Cane Handled Tray, 1900-1927

These four egg cups were produced with a square tray which has four indentations for the egg cups and a cane carrying handle.

Photograph of this
design not available
at press time

Backstamp: Red ink stamp "Wades England" (c.1900-1927)

No.	Description	Colourways	Size	U.S. $	Can. $	U.K. £
1	Egg cups/stand	Egg cups —Black; yellow/red/blue balls	44/153	50.00	70.00	35.00

CLASSIC KINGS/KINGS SHAPE, 1992-1993

This egg cup has an embossed leaf design. For accompanying pieces in this shape see pages 307, 328, 331, 336, 337, 349, 429.

Backstamp: Printed "Wade" between two lines

No.	Description	Colourways	Size	U.S. $	Can. $	U.K. £
1a	Egg cup	Dark green; gold edging	88	4.00	6.00	3.00
1b	Egg cup	White; gold edging	88	4.00	6.00	3.00

C
L
A
S
S
I
C

K
I
N
G
S

IRISH WADE KNURLED SHAPE, c. 1952 - 1960

The shape number of these egg cups is I.P.631

Backstamp: Embossed "Irish Porcelain (curved over Shamrock) Made in Ireland by Wade Co. Armagh" in straight lines

No.	Description	Colourways	Size	U.S. $	Can. $	U.K. £
1a	Egg cup	Blue grey	57	6.00	8.00	4.00
1b	Egg cup	Browny green	57	6.00	8.00	4.00

RIBBED, 1954

The original price of this egg cup was 9d.

Backstamp: Unknown

No.	Description	Colourways	Size	U.S. $	Can. $	U.K. £
1a	Ribbed egg cup	Beige	38	6.00	8.00	4.00
1b	Ribbed egg cup	Crimson	38	8.00	10.00	5.00
1c	Ribbed egg cup	Turquoise	38	8.00	10.00	5.00
1d	Ribbed egg cup	Yellow	38	8.00	10.00	5.00

SANTA CLAUS, 1953-1954

This novelty egg cup (shape no. S.25/30) was modelled as Santa Claus carrying his sack. The open sack forms the egg cup. The original price was 1/9d.

Photograph of this
design not available
at press time

Backstamp: "S.25/30"

No.	Description	Colourways	Size	U.S. $	Can. $	U.K. £
1a	Santa Claus egg cup	Crimson	75	100.00	135.00	70.00
1b	Santa Claus egg cup	Turquoise	75	100.00	135.00	70.00
1c	Santa Claus egg cup	Yellow	75	100.00	135.00	70.00

SWAN, 1955

Backstamp:: Embossed "Made in England" in the hollow of the base

No.	Description	Colourways	Size	U.S. $	Can. $	U.K. £
1a	Swan egg cup	Honey brown	50	40.00	50.00	25.00
1b	Swan egg cup	Pale blue	50	40.00	50.00	25.00
1c	Swan egg cup	Pale green	50	40.00	50.00	25.00
1d	Swan egg cup	Pink	50	40.00	50.00	25.00
1e	Swan egg cup	Turquoise	50	40.00	50.00	25.00
1f	Swan egg cup	Yellow	50	40.00	50.00	25.00

WAVY RIM, 1954

Backstamp: Embossed "BCM/OWL 13"

No.	Description	Colourways	Size	U.S. $	Can. $	U.K. £
1	Egg cup	Beige brown	60	6.00	8.00	4.00

HONEY AND PRESERVE JARS

Wade produced a wide variety of honey and preserve jars. A series of pots with embossed designs of flowers, bees or butterflies and fruit shaped pots were produced between 1934 and 1945. Honey, jam, and preserve pots may have a half circular recess in the lid for a spoon handle.

BARREL, 1953-c.1962

This preserve jar can hold 1lb of jam.

Backstamp: Red transfer printed "Wade England"

No.	Description	Colourways	Size	U.S. $	Can. $	U.K. £
1	Barrel preserve jar	Copper lustre bands	95	40.00	50.00	25.00

B
E
E
H
I
V
E

BEEHIVE, 1937-c.1945

Backstamp: A. Black ink stamp "Flaxman Wade Heath England" (1937-1939)
B. Black or green ink stamp "Wade Heath England" (curved W 1937-c.1945)

No.	Description	Colourways	Size	U.S. $	Can .$	U.K. £
1	Beehive pot	Cream; yellow bands; yellow/ black bee; green grass yellow bee finial on lid	76	45.00	60.00	30.00
2a	Beehive pot	Orange/yellow; yellow bee; green grass; yellow bee finial on lid	82	45.00	60.00	30.00
2b	Beehive pot	Pale blue all over; bee finial on lid	82	45.00	60.00	30.00
2c	Beehive pot	Yellow; yellow bee; green grass; yellow bee finial on lid	82	45.00	60.00	30.00

BIRD ON LID, c. 1937-1945

The only decoration on this plain square honey pot is the bird shaped finial on the lid.

Photograph of this
design not available
at press time

Backstamp: Black ink stamp "Wadeheath England"(1937-1940)

No.	Description	Colourways	Size	U.S. $	Can. $	U.K. £
1	Square pot	Mottled browns; brown bird finial on lid	95	50.00	70.00	35.00

BUTTERFLY, 1937-c.1945

Backstamp: A. Black ink stamp "Wadeheath England"(1937-1940)
          B. Green ink stamp "Wade Heath England"(curved W 1937-1945)

No.	Description	Colourways	Size	U.S. $	Can. $	U.K. £
1a	Butterfly pot	Cream; mauve/yellow/black butterfly on pot and lid; orange flowers	63	45.00	60.00	30.00
1b	Butterfly pot	Cream; mottled dark/light blue; white butterfly on lid	63	45.00	60.00	30.00
1c	Butterfly pot	White; yellow/black butterfly on pot and lid; orange flowers	63	45.00	60.00	30.00
1d	Butterfly pot	White; pink/black butterfly on pot and lid; pink flowers	63	45.00	60.00	30.00
1e	Butterfly pot	White; orange butterfly on pot and lid; orange flowers	63	45.00	60.00	30.00

CLASSIC KINGS/KINGS, 1992-1993

For other pieces in the Classic Kings series please see pages 307, 331, 336, 337, 343, 429.

For an illustration
of this shape
see page 328

Backstamp: Printed "Wade" between two lines

No.	Description	Colourways	Size	U.S. $	Can. $	U.K. £
1a	Preserve jar	Cream	108	12.00	15.00	8.00
1b	Preserve jar	Dark green; gold edging	108	15.00	20.00	10.00
1c	Preserve jar	White	108	12.00	15.00	8.00
1d	Preserve jar	White; gold edging	108	15.00	20.00	10.00

FALSTAFF, c.1972

Wade produced the porcelain part of this honey pot, the silver plated lids with rose bud finials and lion mask handles were produced by the Falstaff Silver Plating Company. A claret jug (see page 291), sugar bowl (page 431) and rose bowl (see *The Charlton Standard Catalogue of Wade Volume 2, Decorative Ware*) were also produced.

Backstamp: Embossed "Wade Falstaff England" with paper label glued on the inside or outside of the item "Falstaff Silver Plated Collection"

No.	Description	Colourways	Size	U.S. $	Can. $	U.K. £
1a	Honey pot, large	Royal blue; silver lid	95	55.00	65.00	30.00
1b	Honey pot, large	White; red roses; silver lid, lion head ring handles	95	35.00	45.00	22.00
1c	Honey pot, large	White; silver grey print; silver lid "Oxford 1874"	95	35.00	45.00	22.00
2a	Honey pot, small	Royal blue; silver lid	75	55.00	65.00	30.00
2b	Honey pot, small	Royal blue; silver lid, lion head ring handles	75	55.00	65.00	30.00

FLOWER, 1934-1939

Backstamp: A. Black ink stamp "Wadeheath England" with lion (1934-1937)
B. Black ink stamp "Flaxman Ware Hand Made Pottery by Wadeheath England"(1935-1937)
C. Black ink stamp "Flaxman Wade Heath England" (1937-1939)

No.	Description	Colourways	Size	U.S. $	Can. $	U.K. £
1a	Iris pot, large	Cream; orange/yellow irises; green leaves orange flower finial on lid	100	60.00	75.00	35.00
1b	Iris pot, large	Brown all over	100	45.00	55.00	25.00
2a	Iris pot, small	Cream; pale and dark pink flowers; dark green leaves; dark pink flower finial on lid	88	60.00	75.00	35.00
2b	Iris pot, small	Cream; lilac/yellow flowers; green leaves; lilac flower finial on lid	88	60.00	75.00	35.00
2c	Iris pot, small	Mottled green/beige	88	45.00	55.00	25.00
2d	Iris pot, small	Mottled pale green/yellow	88	45.00	55.00	25.00
2e	Iris pot, small	Turquoise/ beige	88	45.00	55.00	25.00
3	Pansy pot, large	Cream; pink and white pansy flowers; pink flower finial on lid	100	60.00	75.00	35.00

FLUTED, 1954

The fluted honey jar was produced by Wade during the early part of 1954 and was advertised as: "Base only flower bowl in green, beige or yellow at 2/6d each. Complete with lid "fluted honey jar" in green, beige of yellow 3/11d."

Backstamp: Embossed "S.25/35"

No.	Description	Colourways	Size	U.S. $	Can. $	U.K. £
1a	Fluted honey jar	Beige	59	20.00	30.00	15.00
1b	Fluted honey jar	Green	59	20.00	30.00	15.00
1c	Fluted honey jar	Yellow	59	20.00	30.00	15.00

FRUIT, c.1938-1945

Backstamp: Black or green ink stamp "Wadeheath England" (1937-c.1948)

No.	Description	Colourways	Size	U.S. $	Can. $	U.K. £
1a	Apple pot	Streaked maroon/yellow; green leaves finial on lid	88	45.00	60.00	30.00
1b	Apple pot	Streaked maroon/ brown/yellow; green leaves finial on lid	88	45.00	60.00	30.00
2	Orange pot	Orange; green leaf finial on lid	88	45.00	60.00	30.00
3a	Pear pot	Yellow/red streaks; green leaves finial on lid	108	45.00	60.00	30.00
3b	Pear pot	Browny/grey streaks; green leaves finial on lid	108	45.00	60.00	30.00
4	Pineapple pot	Yellow; green leaves finial on lid	108	45.00	60.00	30.00

IRISH WADE KNURLED, 1971-1976

This knurled preserve jar (Shape No. I.P.23) has a three row design of embossed and impressed dots and shamrocks.

Backstamp: Impressed "Irish Porcelain (curved over large shamrock) Made in Ireland" in straight line (with or without potters initial included)

No.	Description	Colourways	Size	U.S. $	Can. $	U.K. £
1	Knurled preserve jar	Green brown	70	30.00	40.00	20.00

ORCHARD FRUITS, c.1950-c.1960

Each of these pots was sold with a white tray with a matching red or yellow band. There were four different fruit designs available: apples, pears, plums or strawberries.

Backstamp: Red printed "Wade England"

No.	Description	Colourways	Size	U.S. $	Can. $	U.K. £
1a	Preserve pot/ tray	Pot —White; red band lid; multi-coloured apple print Tray —White; red band	125/110	35.00	45.00	25.00
1b	Preserve pot/ tray	Pot — White; yellow band lid; multi-coloured apple print; Tray —White; yellow band	125/110	35.00	45.00	25.00
1c	Preserve pot/ tray	Pot —White; red band lid; multi-coloured pear print Tray —White; red band	125/110	35.00	45.00	25.00
1d	Preserve pot/ tray	Pot — White; yellow band lid; multi-coloured pear print; Tray —White; yellow band	125/110	35.00	45.00	25.00
1e	Preserve pot/ tray	Pot —White; red band lid; multi-coloured plum print Tray —White; red band	125/110	35.00	45.00	25.00
1f	Preserve pot/ tray	Pot — White; yellow band lid; multi-coloured plum print; Tray —White; yellow band	125/110	35.00	45.00	25.00
1g	Preserve pot/ tray	Pot —White; red band lid; multi-coloured strawberry print; Tray —White; red band	125/110	35.00	45.00	25.00
1h	Preserve pot/ tray	Pot — White; yellow band lid; multi-coloured strawberry print; Tray —White; yellow band	125/110	35.00	45.00	25.00

PARTRIDGE IN A PEAR TREE, 1992

Backstamp: Printed red circular "Royal Victoria Pottery Staffordshire Wade England"

No.	Description	Colourways	Size	U.S. $	Can. $	U.K. £
1	Preserve pot	White; multi-coloured print	114	12.00	20.00	10.00

RIBBED, 1937-c.1940

These ribbed shaped pots can be found in all over one colour glazes or with hand painted designs on them.

Backstamp: Black or green ink stamp "Wade Heath England" (curved W 1937-c.1940)

No.	Description	Colourways	Size	U.S. $	Can. $	U.K. £
1a	Preserve pot	Pale green matt glaze	65	18.00	25.00	12.00
1b	Preserve pot	Cream; brown tree; green leaves/grass; orange finial	65	18.00	25.00	12.00
1c	Preserve pot	Cream; brown fence; green leaves/ grass; orange finial and small flowers	65	18.00	25.00	12.00

RIBBED CROSS BAND, c.1942

These embossed rib pots have a broad angled cross band design and have been found in all over one-colour glazes and with hand- painted designs.

Backstamp: A. Black or green ink stamp "Wadeheath England" (1937-c.1945)
B. Green ink stamp "Wade Heath England" (curved W 1937-c.1945)

No.	Description	Colourways	Size	U.S. $	Can. $	U.K. £
1a	Preserve pot	Cream; orange flowers/green brown tree on angled cross band	65	18.00	25.00	12.00
1b	Preserve pot	Mottled orange/grey	65	18.00	25.00	12.00
1c	Preserve pot	Yellow and green; silver angled cross band	65	18.00	25.00	12.00

ROUND HANDPAINTED, c.1945

These round pots have a smooth surface and hand-painted designs

Photograph of this
shape not available
at press time

Backstamp: Black or green ink stamp "Wadeheath England" (straight W c.1945)

No.	Description	Colourways	Size	U.S. $	Can. $	U.K. £
1a	Preserve pot	Bright orange, green and black stripes	63	18.00	25.00	12.00
1b	Preserve pot	Yellow pot; red flower; green leaves final on lid	63	18.00	25.00	12.00

SHAPE UNKNOWN

CROSS BANDED DESIGN

Backstamp: Impressed "Irish Porcelain" (curved over a large shamrock) "Made in Ireland" in straight line (with or without potters initial)

No.	Description	Colourways	Size	U.S. $	Can. $	U.K. £
1	Preserve jar	Green brown	65	18.00	25.00	12.00

MISCELLANEOUS POTS

CAVIAR POTS, 1972-1977

These Caviar pots were produced in large quantities by Wade Ireland between 1972-1977 for W.G White of London and also for Harrods of Knightsbridge.

Backstamp: A. Handwritten "2"
B. Handwritten "4 W.G. White London" with impressed "Wade Porcelain Co. Armagh"
C. Handwritten "8 W.G. White London" with impressed "Wade Porcelain Co. Armagh"
D. Impressed "Wade Porcelain Co. Armagh"

No.	Description	Colourways	Size	U.S. $	Can. $	U.K. £
1	Pot, 8 oz	Stone coloured pot, purple/gold fish; gold seaweed	88 x 101	60.00	70.00	35.00
2	Pot, 4 oz		101 x 70	50.00	60.00	30.00
3	Pot, 2 oz		63 x 63	50.00	60.00	30.00
4	Pot, 4 oz, Harrods	White pot; black lettering	95	50.00	60.00	30.00

CELTIC CROSS POT, c.1970-1987

This heavy round pot produced by Wade Ireland has a looped handle on the lid and on each side of the pot and resembles a casserole pot. It has an embossed Celtic cross and inscription on the front.

Photograph of this
shape not available
at press time

Backstamp: Embossed "Irish Porcelain (curved over large shamrock & crown) Wade Ireland" in straight line

No.	Description	Colourways	Size	U.S. $	Can. $	U.K. £
1	Celtic cross pot	Browny green	133	60.00	70.00	35.00

Bowls and Dishes

SHAPE NAME INDEX

Bowls

Dishes

BOWLS

BRICK BOWLS, 1937 - c.1945

This round bowl has an embossed brick wall design and was produced in an assortment of colours and sizes. For a basket in similar design see *The Charlton Standard Catalogue of Wade, Volume Two Decorative Ware.*

Backstamp: A. Black ink stamp "Flaxman Wade Heath England" (1937-1939)
B. Black ink stamp "Wade England Flaxman" (c.1945-c.1948)

No.	Description	Colourways	Size	U.S. $	Can. $	U.K. £
1	Fruit bowl, extra large	Mottled blue	300	40.00	55.00	30.00
2	Fruit bowl, large		225	40.00	55.00	30.00
3	Fruit bowl, medium		205	38.00	50.00	25.00
4	Fruit bowl, small		195	38.00	50.00	25.00
5	Fruit bowl, large	Mottled green	225	40.00	55.00	30.00
6	Fruit bowl, extra large	Mottled yellow/green	300	40.00	55.00	30.00
7	Fruit bowl, medium		205	38.00	50.00	25.00
8	Fruit bowl, extra large	Off white	300	40.00	55.00	30.00

COPPER LUSTRE BOWLS, c.1938-c.1965

The following copper lustre bowls have no shape name and are listed in a Wade Heath sales catalogue as "Assorted Hand Painted Patterns With Copper Lustre Finish." Because Copper Lustre Wares were costly to produce they were issued in limited quantities only, they were first issued in the late 1930s and re-introduced at various times throughout the next thirty years.

ASTER DESIGN

Backstamp: Gold printed "Wade Made in England Hand painted" (1953-c.1962)

No.	Description	Colourways	Size	U.S. $	Can. $	U.K. £
1	Bowl, large	Copper; pink flowers; yellow/green leaves	150	22.00	30.00	15.00
2	Finger bowl		101	22.00	30.00	15.00

BLUE TULIP DESIGN

Backstamp: Green ink stamp "Wade England" (c.1945-c.1948)

No.	Description	Colourways	Size	U.S. $	Can. $	U.K. £
1	Finger bowl	White; pale blue tulip; grey leaves; mother of pearl and silver highlighting	101	22.00	30.00	15.00

CLOVER DESIGN

Backstamp: Green ink stamp "Wade England" (crossed W c.1945-c.1948)

No.	Description	Colourways	Size	U.S. $	Can. $	U.K. £
1	Bowl, large	Copper; pink/yellow/green clover and leaves	150	25.00	35.00	18.00
2	Bowl, small		127	22.00	30.00	15.00
3	Finger bowl		101	22.00	30.00	15.00

COPPER DESIGN

Backstamp: Green ink stamp "Harvest Ware Wade England" (c.1948-c.1952)

No.	Description	Colourways	Size	U.S. $	Can. $	U.K. £
1	Finger bowl	Copper	101	12.00	15.00	8.00

DAISY DESIGN

Backstamp: Green ink stamp "Harvest Ware Wade England" (c.1948-c.1952)

No.	Description	Colourways	Size	U.S. $	Can. $	U.K. £
1	Finger bowl	Cream; maroon/yellow daisy; green/brown leaves	101	22.00	30.00	15.00

FUSCHIA DESIGN

Photograph of this
design not available
at press time

Backstamp: Green ink stamp "Wade England" (crossed W c.1945-c.1948)

No.	Description	Colourways	Size	U.S. $	Can. $	U.K. £
1	Finger bowl	Pearl lustre; large red/yellow fuchsia flowers; green leaves	101	25.00	40.00	20.00

GEORGIAN OAK DESIGN

Backstamp: **A.** Gold printed "Wade Made in England Hand painted" (1953-c.1962)
B. Red printed "Wade England" (1953-c.1962)
C. Green ink stamp "Wade England" (crossed W c.1948-1953) (Four point bowl only)

No.	Description	Colourways	Size	U.S. $	Can. $	U.K. £
1a	Bowl, large	Copper bowl; white oak leaves and acorns	150	25.00	35.00	18.00
1b	Bowl, large	Copper bowl; white bands, oak leaves and acorns	150	25.00	35.00	18.00
1c	Bowl, large	White bowl; copper rim, oak leaves and acorns	150	25.00	35.00	18.00
2	Four-point bowl	Copper bowl; white oak leaves & acorns	150	30.00	40.00	20.00

OAK LEAF AND BERRIES DESIGN

Backstamp: Gold printed "Wade Made in England Hand painted" (1953-c.1962)

No.	Description	Colourways	Size	U.S. $	Can. $	U.K. £
1	Bowl, large	White bowl; copper rim, leaves, berries	150	25.00	35.00	18.00
2	Finger bowl		101	15.00	20.00	10.00

PEONIES DESIGN

For an illustration
of this design
see page 314

Backstamp: Unknown

No.	Description	Colourways	Size	U.S. $	Can. $	U.K. £
1a	Finger bowl	Cream bowl; copper rim; maroon/yellow flower; green/brown leaves	101	22.00	30.00	15.00
1b	Finger bowl	Cream bowl; copper rim; blue/yellow flower; green/brown leaves	101	22.00	30.00	15.00

POPPY DESIGN

For an illustration
of this design
see page 215

Backstamp: Green ink stamp "Harvest Ware Wade England" (c.1948-c.1952)

No.	Description	Colourways	Size	U.S. $	Can. $	U.K. £
1	Finger bowl	Cream bowl; copper rim; maroon/mauve flowers; green/brown leaves	101	22.00	30.00	15.00

ROSE DESIGN

Backstamp: Green printed "Wade England" (1961)

No.	Description	Colourways	Size	U.S. $	Can. $	U.K. £
1	Bowl, small	White bowl; copper rim; blue flowers/leaves	127	22.00	30.00	15.00

COPPER LUSTRE

COUNTRYWARE BOWLS, c.1970-1984

This bowl was produced in the Wade Ireland Pottery, Portadown, Northern Ireland. For matching items see pages 397 and 409.

Backstamp: Impressed circular "Design Wade Country Ware Made in Ireland"

No.	Description	Colourways	Size	U.S. $	Can. $	U.K. £
1	Soup bowl	Amber	127	6.00	8.00	4.00

C
O
U
N
T
R
Y
W
A
R
E

FLARED BOWLS, c.1937-c.1945

These bowls are narrow at the base and flare out at the top.

BANDED DESIGN

Backstamp: Impressed "Flaxman Wade Heath England" (1937-1939)

No.	Description	Colourways	Size	U.S. $	Can. $	U.K. £
1	Fruit bowl, large	Green bands; brown lines	260	40.00	55.00	30.00
2	Fruit bowl, medium		230	40.00	55.00	30.00
3	Fruit bowl, small		195	35.00	50.00	25.00

BLOSSOM DESIGN

The blossom decoration was also used on Orb tablewares and Dandy cream jugs and sugar bowls.

Backstamp: Impressed "Flaxman Wade Heath England" (1937-1939)

No.	Description	Colourways	Size	U.S. $	Can. $	U.K. £
1	Fruit bowl, medium	White; green flower; grey leaves	230	40.00	55.00	30.00

F
L
A
R
E
D

MOTTLED DESIGN

This all over one colour mottled glaze is similar to the Flaxman ware decoration seen on decorative wares.

Backstamp: A. Black ink stamp "Flaxman Wade Heath England" (1937-1939)
B. Black ink stamp "Wade England Flaxman" (c.1945-c.1948)

No.	Description	Colourways	Size	U.S. $	Can. $	U.K. £
1	Fruit bowl, large	Mottled yellow/green	260	35.00	50.00	25.00
2a	Fruit bowl, small		195	35.00	50.00	25.00
2b	Fruit bowl, small	Mottled cream/green	195	35.00	50.00	25.00

SPRINGTIME DESIGN

This multi-coloured transfer print of a large parrot tulip and other flowers was used a number of times by Wadeheath on Regency and other Tablewares (see page 135).

Backstamp: Green ink stamp "Wade Heath England" (straight W c.1945-c.1952)

No.	Description	Colourways	Size	U.S. $	Can. $	U.K. £
1	Bowl, large	White; green band; multi-coloured flowers print	230	35.00	50.00	25.00
2	Bowl, small		195	40.00	60.00	30.00

F
L
A
R
E
D

HEXAGONAL BOWLS

Backstamp: Ink stamp "Wadeheath Orcadia Ware British Made"

No.	Description	Colourways	Size	U.S. $	Can. $	U.K. £
1	Fruit bowl	Brown/orange/yellow	155	55.00	70.00	35.00

IRISH WADE SHAPE NO. I.P. 74, c.1950
Porridge Bowls

Backstamp: Printed "Irish Porcelain" (slanted over shamrock) Wade Co Armagh" in straight line

No.	Description	Colourways	Size	U.S. $	Can. $	U.K. £
1a	Duck hunter	Blue/green; multi-coloured print	127	25.00	35.00	15.00
1b	Flying ducks		127	25.00	35.00	15.00
1c	Flying pheasants		127	25.00	35.00	15.00
1d	Fox hunter		127	25.00	35.00	15.00
1e	Leprechauns and mushrooms		127	35.00	45.00	22.00
1f	Stags head		127	25.00	35.00	15.00

IRISH WADE SHAPE NO. UNKNOWN

This unusual child's porridge bowl, which is undecorated, has been covered in an outer layer of copper coloured metal.

Backstamp: Printed "Irish Porcelain (slanted over shamrock) Wade Co Armagh" in straight line

No.	Description	Colourways	Size	U.S. $	Can. $	U.K. £
1	Porridge bowl	Copper layer; blue/green bowl	165	25.00	35.00	15.00

IRISH WADE SHAPE NO I.P. 76
Nut Bowls

I
R
I
S
H

W
A
D
E

Backstamp: **A.** Impressed "Irish Porcelain (curved over large shamrock) Made in Ireland" in straight line
B. Impressed "Irish Porcelain (slanted over shamrock) "Wade Co Armagh" in straight line

No.	Description	Colourways	Size	U.S. $	Can. $	U.K. £
1a	Colleen and Cottage "Ireland"	Blue/grey; multi-coloured print; black lettering	165	25.00	30.00	15.00
1b	Duck hunter	Blue/grey; multi-coloured print	165	25.00	30.00	15.00
1c	Finn McCaul		165	25.00	30.00	15.00
1d	Flying ducks		165	25.00	30.00	15.00

OCTAGONAL BOWLS, 1935-1937

FLORAL DESIGN

Backstamp: Black ink stamp "Wadeheath Ware England"

No.	Description	Colourways	Size	U.S. $	Can. $	U.K. £
1	Dessert bowl	Cream; large blue/orange flowers; green leaves	159	10.00	12.00	6.00
2	Fruit serving bowl		248	25.00	30.00	15.00

POWDERED WARE ODD-SHAPED BOWLS

These odd-shaped bowls have four, five, six and eight points. The four and five point bowls resemble Catherine Wheels, the others flower heads. The powdered ware bowls have a band of speckled glaze as if dusted with powder hence the name Powdered Ware. This type of decoration was also used on Orb Tableware (see page 115). A multi-coloured print of flowers on a white background is in the centre of each bowl and the rims are highlighted in gold. Similar shapes were used in the Bramble Ware series (see page 15).

P
O
W
D
E
R
E
D

W
A
R
E

Backstamp: Green ink stamp "Wade England" (crossed W c.1948-1953)

No.	Description	Colourways	Size	U.S. $	Can. $	U.K. £
1a	Four point bowl	Gold rim; powdered blue band; white centre; multi-coloured print of flowers	150	30.00	40.00	20.00
2a	Five point bowl		177	35.00	45.00	22.00
3a	Six point bowl		127	40.00	50.00	25.00
1b	Four point bowl	Gold rim; powdered green band; white centre; multi-coloured print of flowers	150	30.00	40.00	20.00
2b	Five point bowl		177	35.00	45.00	22.00
3b	Six point bowl		127	40.00	50.00	25.00
1c	Four point bowl	Gold rim; powdered maroon band; white centre; multi-coloured print of flowers	150	30.00	40.00	20.00
2c	Five point bowl		177	35.00	45.00	22.00
3c	Six point bowl		127	40.00	50.00	25.00

ROUND BOWLS

BUTTERFLY DESIGN

Backstamp: Orange ink stamp "Wadeheath England" with lion (1933-1934)

No.	Description	Colourways	Size	U.S. $	Can. $	U.K. £
1	Fruit bowl	Cream; large blue flowers; green leaves; small orange flowers; brown butterfly	205	55.00	80.00	40.00

CROWN DERBY DESIGN

Backstamp: Orange ink stamp "Wadeheath England" with lion (1933-1934)

No.	Description	Colourways	Size	U.S. $	Can. $	U.K. £
1	Fruit bowl	White; cobalt blue panels with gold decoration on top half; orange and gold decoration on bottom	205	55.00	80.00	40.00

FLAXMAN WARE DESIGN

Backstamp: Black ink stamp "Flaxman Ware Hand Made Pottery by Wadeheath England" (1935-1937)

No.	Description	Colourways	Size	U.S. $	Can. $	U.K. £
1	Fruit bowl	Mottled blue	205	55.00	80.00	40.00

FLORAL DESIGN, 1933-1934

Backstamp: Orange ink stamp "Wadeheath England" with lion (1933-1934)

No.	Description	Colourways	Size	U.S. $	Can. $	U.K. £
1	Fruit bowl	Cream; orange band rim; large blue flowers; green leaves; orange/black splashes	205	45.00	55.00	30.00

ROUND WITH FLARED RIM

TARTAN DESIGN, 1961-c.1975

Backstamp: Black circular "Royal Victoria Pottery Wade England"

No.	Description	Colourways	Size	U.S. $	Can. $	U.K. £
1	Dessert bowl	Streaky green; dark green/purple/maroon tartan bands	162	10.00	12.00	6.00
2	Fruit serving bowl		290	40.00	60.00	30.00

STAG SHAPE, c.1948 - c.1960

On some of the copper lustre pieces the design is barely visible because of the thick glaze. The round bowl carries the Shape No. 171. For jugs in this shape see page 324.

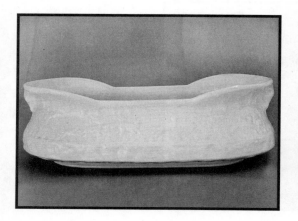 

Backstamp: **A.** Green ink stamp "Harvest Ware Wade England" (c.1948-c.1953)
B. Green ink stamp "Wade England" with impressed "171" (c.1948-c.1953)

No.	Description	Colourways	Size	U.S. $	Can. $	U.K. £
1a	Fruit bowl, oval	Copper lustre	280	75.00	100.00	50.00
1b	Fruit bowl, oval	Cream	280	55.00	80.00	40.00
2	Fruit bowl, round	Copper lustre	90	45.00	60.00	30.00

TRIANGULAR BOWLS

FLOWER DESIGN, 1934-1940

Backstamp: A. Black ink stamp "Wadeheath Ware England" (1934-1937)
B. Green ink stamp "Wade Heath England" (round W 1937-1940)

No.	Description	Colourways	Size	U.S. $	Can. $	U.K. £
1	Dessert bowl	White; brown dashed edging, stems; yellow/ orange flowers; green leaves	162	8.00	10.00	5.00
2a	Fruit serving bowl	White; brown edging, stems; yellow/orange flowers; green leaves	245	20.00	25.00	12.00
2b	Fruit serving bowl	Cream; yellow/green flowers; black leaves	245	20.00	25.00	12.00

DISHES

HEXAGONAL DISH

SPIDER WEB DESIGN

This design was also used on Ross shaped jugs (see page 322).

Backstamp: Green ink stamp "Wade Heath England"

No.	Description	Colourways	Size	U.S. $	Can. $	U.K. £
1	Dish	Cream; black rim/web; brown tree; red poppies; green grass/leaves	130	15.00	20.00	10.00

OVAL DISH

ASTER DESIGN

Backstamp: **A.** Green ink stamp "Wade England" (crossed W c.1945-c.1948)
B. Gold printed semi circular "Wade Made in England Hand Painted" (1953-c.1965)

No.	Description	Colourways	Size	U.S. $	Can. $	U.K. £
1	Oval dish, large	Copper; pink flowers; yellow/green leaves	200	35.00	45.00	25.00
2	Oval dish, small		127	30.00	40.00	20.00

CLOVER DESIGN

For an illustration
of this design
see page 363

Backstamp: Green ink stamp "Wade England" (crossed W c.1945-c.1948)

No.	Description	Colourways	Size	U.S. $	Can. $	U.K. £
1	Oval dish	Copper; pink flowers; yellow/green leaves	254	35.00	45.00	25.00

POWDERED WARE ODD-SHAPED DISHES

These odd-shaped dishes bowls have two or four rounded points. The powdered ware dishes have a band of speckled glaze as if dusted with powder hence the name Powdered Ware (this type of decoration was also used on Orb Tablewares, see page 115). A multi-coloured print of flowers on a white background is in the centre of each dish, the rims are highlighted in gold. Similar shapes were used in the Bramble Ware series (see page 15).

Backstamp: Green ink stamp "Wade England" (crossed W c.1948-1953)

No.	Description	Colourways	Size	U.S. $	Can. $	U.K. £
1a	Two point oval dish	Gold rim; powdered blue band; white centre; multi-coloured print of flowers	254	30.00	40.00	20.00
2a	Two point oval dish		305	35.00	45.00	25.00
3a	Four point oval dish		205	30.00	40.00	20.00
1b	Two point oval dish	Gold rim; powdered green band; white centre; multi-coloured print of flowers	254	30.00	40.00	20.00
2b	Two point oval dish		305	35.00	45.00	25.00
3b	Four point oval dish		205	30.00	40.00	20.00
1c	Two point oval dish	Gold rim; powdered maroon band; white centre; multi-coloured print of flowers	254	30.00	40.00	20.00
2c	Two point oval dish		305	35.00	45.00	25.00
3c	Four point oval dish		205	30.00	40.00	20.00

P O W D E R E D W A R E

Plates

No matching items have been reported for the following cake stands and plates though it is assumed they were once part of a tea or breakfast set, the design "names" are unknown.

SHAPE NAME INDEX

CAKE PLATES

TULIPS DESIGN

Photograph of design
not available
at press time

Backstamp: Printed "Wade England" (1953-c.1962)

No.	Description	Colourways	Size	U.S. $	Can. $	U.K. £
1	Cake plate	Black; white rim; orange/cream tulips; small purple flowers; green leaves	242	40.00	50.00	25.00

TULIPS WITH PEONY DESIGN

Backstamp: Printed "Wade England" (1953-c.1962)

No.	Description	Colourways	Size	U.S. $	Can. $	U.K. £
1	Cake plate	Black; white rim; orange/cream tulip; dark red peony; small purple flowers; green leaves	242	40.00	50.00	25.00

CAKE STANDS

BLOSSOM DESIGN

This cake stand has the same Blossom decoration used on "Orb" tablewares and Dandy cream jugs and sugar bowls. The stand has an attached chrome foot which is fixed with a screw through the middle of the plate.

For an illustration
of this design
see page 106

Backstamp: Green ink stamp "Wade Heath England" (1937-1940)

No.	Description	Colourways	Size	U.S. $	Can. $	U.K. £
1	Cake stand	White; green flower; grey leaves; chrome foot	195	40.00	50.00	25.00

LEAVES DESIGN

There is a leaf design on this black two-tiered cake stand which has a metal handle through the centre of the plates, the colours are similar to the "Tulip" cake plate.

Backstamp: Red printed "Wade England" (1953-c.1962)

No.	Description	Colourways	Size	U.S. $	Can. $	U.K. £
1	Two-tier cake plate	Black; white rim; orange/cream/green/ blue/purple leaves	248	35.00	50.00	25.00

POPPY DESIGN

The design name for this embossed "Poppy Flower" cake stand or bon bon dish is unknown, it has a moulded foot and an embossed design of poppy flowers and leaves.

Backstamp: Ink stamp "Flaxman Wade Heath England" (1937-1939)

No.	Description	Colourways	Size	U.S. $	Can. $	U.K. £
1	Cake stand	Mottled creamy yellow/pink	153	65.00	90.00	45.00
2a	Footed cake stand	Blue/yellow/lilac/brown	153	65.00	90.00	45.00
2b	Footed cake stand	Mottled green	153	65.00	90.00	45.00
2c	Footed cake stand	Mottled yellow/blue	153	65.00	90.00	45.00

SPECKLED DESIGN

The design name of this speckled cake stand is unknown, it is similar to the Flaxman ware designs.

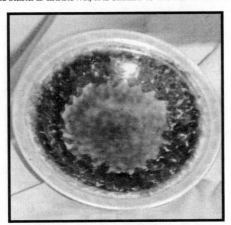

Backstamp: Ink stamp "Wadeheath Ware England" (1934-1937)

No.	Description	Colourways	Size	U.S. $	Can. $	U.K. £
1	Cake stand	Yellow banded rim; brown speckles; green centre	165	50.00	70.00	35.00

MISCELLANEOUS PLATES

Some of the following small plates resemble the Flair and Orb shapes with a rim or Mode shape which has no rim. No other matching items have been reported to date.

FLAIR TYPE PLATES WITH RIM

BLACKPOOL DESIGN

Backstamp: Green ink stamp "Wade England" (crossed W c.1948-1953)

No.	Description	Colourways	Size	U.S. $	Can. $	U.K. £
1	Plate	White; multi-coloured print of Blackpool Tower in yellow horseshoe	175	12.00	15.00	8.00

PRIMROSE DESIGN

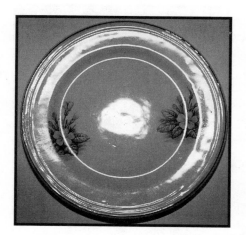

Backstamp: Black ink stamp circular "Royal Victoria Pottery Wade England" (c.1952-c.1965)

No.	Description	Colourways	Size	U.S. $	Can. $	U.K. £
1	Plate	White; green rim; yellow primrose flowers; green leaves	165	8.00	10.00	5.00

MODE TYPE PLATES NO RIM

CHECK AND FLOWERS DESIGN

Backstamp: Black ink stamp circular "Royal Victoria Pottery Wade England" (c.1952-c.1965)

No.	Description	Colourways	Size	U.S. $	Can. $	U.K. £
1	Plate	White; dark green check/flowers/leaves	153	8.00	10.00	5.00

LILY OF THE VALLEY DESIGN

Backstamp: Black ink stamp circular "Royal Victoria Pottery Wade England" (c.1952-c.1965)

No.	Description	Colourways	Size	U.S. $	Can. $	U.K. £
1	Plate	White; white flowers; green leaves; pink grass	153	8.00	10.00	5.00

LOOPS DESIGN

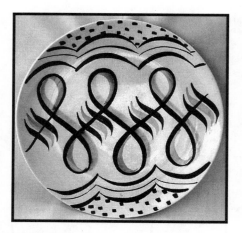

Backstamp: Red printed "Wade England" (1953-c.1962)

No.	Description	Colourways	Size	U.S. $	Can. $	U.K. £
1	Plate	White; yellow/black/maroon loops; black dots	153	8.00	10.00	5.00

MOULDED HAND GRIP PLATE

FISH DESIGN

This unusual plate with abstract fish faces, has indented moulded hand grips on two sides and resembles the Mode style TV plates.

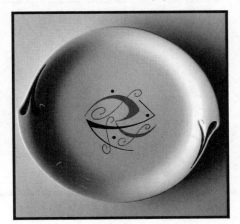

Backstamp: Handpainted in pink "Flair" with black printed "A Louis Gordon Production Made in England" (c.1965)

No.	Description	Colourways	Size	U.S. $	Can. $	U.K. £
1	Plate	White; silver leaf indents; pink/black faces	248	8.00	10.00	5.00

WOVEN EMBOSSED RIM

PALE BLUE DESIGN

Backstamp: Ink stamp "Wade England" (c.1945-1953)

No.	Description	Colourways	Size	U.S. $	Can. $	U.K. £
1	Plate	Pale blue	205	12.00	15.00	8.00

BISCUIT BARRELS, STORAGE CONTAINERS, AND TEA CADDIES

SHAPE NAME INDEX

BISCUIT BARRELS

BEE SHAPE

WINDMILL DESIGN

Backstamp: Orange ink stamp "Wade England" with lion (1927-1933)

No.	Description	Colourways	Size	U.S. $	Can. $	U.K.£
1	Biscuit barrel	Cream; multi-coloured handpainted windmill, scenery	165	70.00	90.00	45.00

DAVENPORT SHAPE, 1927-1933

The biscuit barrel is round with straight sides and has rounded projections on each side onto which a cane handle is fixed.

CROWN DERBY DESIGN

For an illustration
of this design
see page 158

Backstamp: Orange ink stamp "Wade England" with lion (1927-1933)

No.	Description	Colourways	Size	U.S. $	Can. $	U.K.£
1	Biscuit barrel	Cobalt blue panels with gold decoration on top half; orange/blue and gold decoration on bottom	127	75.00	100.00	50.00

STAGECOACH DESIGN

Photograph of this
design not available
at press time

Backstamp: Orange ink stamp "Wade England" with lion (1927-1933)

No.	Description	Colourways	Size	U.S. $	Can. $	U.K. £
1	Biscuit barrel	Multi-coloured print of stagecoach and country scene on top half; cream on bottom half	127	45.00	60.00	30.00

B
E
E

IRISH WADE SHAPE NO I.P. 94, c.1985-c.1988

This Irish Wade biscuit barrel has three rows of knurls and shamrocks on the barrel and has a heavily embossed design on the lid which twists into a groove to seal.

Backstamp: Impressed "Irish Porcelain (curved over shamrock with or without potters initial in shamrock) Made in Ireland" (c.1985)

No.	Description	Colourways	Size	U.S. $	Can. $	U.K. £
1	Biscuit barrel, large	Blue green brown	140	50.00	70.00	35.00
2	Biscuit barrel, small	Blue-grey	114	50.00	70.00	35.00

UNKNOWN SHAPE

COBALT BLUE DESIGN, 1927-1933

This round biscuit barrel is cobalt blue with gold bands.

Photograph not
available at
press time

Backstamp: Orange ink stamp " Wade England" with lion (1927-1933)

No.	Description	Colourways	Size	U.S. $	Can. $	U.K. £
1	Biscuit barrel	Cobalt blue barrel; gold bands	127	70.00	90.00	45.00

Text in left margin: I R I S H W A D E

STORAGE CONTAINERS

CLASSIC KINGS/KINGS, 1992-1993

For an illustration of these containers please see page 328. For other Classic Kings items see pages 307, 331, 336, 337, 343, 349 and 429. The utensil jars are similar to the storage containers except they lack lids.

Backstamp: Printed "Wade" between two lines

No.	Description	Colourways	Size	U.S. $	Can. $	U.K. £
1a	Storage jar, large	Cream	190	15.00	20.00	10.00
2a	Storage jar, small		140	12.00	15.00	8.00
3a	Utensil jar		unknown	10.00	12.00	6.00
1b	Storage jar, large	Dark green; gold edging	190	18.00	25.00	12.00
2b	Storage jar, small		140	15.00	20.00	10.00
3b	Utensil jar	White	unknown	10.00	12.00	6.00
1c	Storage jar, large		190	15.00	20.00	10.00
2c	Storage jar, small		140	12.00	15.00	8.00
1d	Storage jar, large	White; gold edging	190	18.00	25.00	12.00
2d	Storage jar, small		140	15.00	20.00	10.00

COUNTRYWARE, c.1978-1984

The following cookware items are all in an amber brown glaze and were produced in the Wade Ireland Pottery, Portadown, in Northern Ireland. For matching items see pages 337 and 397.

Backstamp: Impressed circular "Design Wade Country Ware Made in Ireland"

No.	Description	Colourways	Size	U.S. $	Can. $	U.K. £
1	Storage jar, large	Amber	140	20.00	30.00	15.00
2	Storage jar, small		114	20.00	30.00	15.00

RIVIERA, c.1958-c.1962

These jars are the same shape as those used for the Topline series of pots, dishes and jars (see *The Charlton Standard Catalogue of Wade Volume Two, Decorative Ware)*. The jars can be found with the same print on the front and back or two related prints.

R
I
V
I
E
R
A

Backstamp: Printed "Wade England"

No.	Description	Colourways	Size	U.S. $	Can. $	U.K. £
1a	Storage jar, large	Pale blue; multi-coloured print of woman with bouquet of flowers/couple drinking	170	25.00	35.00	18.00
1b	Storage jar, large	Yellow; multi-coloured print of woman drinking/woman with parrot in cage	170	25.00	35.00	18.00
1c	Storage jar, large	Yellow; multi-coloured print of woman with black cat/couple drinking	170	25.00	35.00	18.00
2	Storage jar, small	White; multi-coloured print of couple drinking/woman with parrot in cage	145	25.00	35.00	18.00

VILLAGE STORES, 1982-1986

The original price for these canisters was £7.00. Please see pages 334, 336 and 340 for matching pieces.

Backstamp: Black printed "Village Stores by Wade Staffordshire England"

No.	Description	Colourways	Size	U.S. $	Can. $	U.K. £
1	Coffee canister	Orange brown tile roof; white canister; multi-coloured print; black lettering "The Coffee House"	191	70.00	80.00	40.00
2	Flour canister	Yellow brown tile roof; white canister; multi-coloured print; yellow lettering "Baker B. Loaf Cakes"	191	70.00	80.00	40.00
3	Sugar canister	Maroon tile roof; white canister; multi-coloured print; black lettering "Ice Cream Mrs. Smiths Sweets"	191	70.00	80.00	40.00
4	Tea canister	Blue grey tile roof; white canister; multi-coloured print; black lettering "Ye Old Tearoom"	191	70.00	80.00	40.00

TEA CADDIES

CHRISTMAS, 1987-1989

Snowmen, Poinsettia, Chinese Rose

Backstamp: Red printed "Wade England"

CHINESE ROSE DESIGN

No.	Description	Colourways	Size	U.S. $	Can. $	U.K. £
1	Tea caddy	White; pink/orange flowers; green leaves	90	25.00	35.00	18.00

POINSETTIA DESIGN

No.	Description	Colourways	Size	U.S. $	Can. $	U.K. £
1b	Tea caddy	White; red/white poinsettia flowers and berries; green holly leaves	90	25.00	35.00	18.00

SNOWMEN DESIGN

No.	Description	Colourways	Size	U.S. $	Can. $	U.K. £
1c	Tea caddy	White; white snowmen; light brown hats; red striped scarves; blue sky	90	25.00	35.00	18.00

DOUBLE CADDY

This unusual caddy with a centre handle was probably intended for both green tea and black tea which would then be measured and mixed together in the teapot to the makers individual taste.

CROWN DERBY DESIGN

Backstamp: Orange ink stamp "Wade England" with lion

No.	Description	Colourways	Size	U.S. $	Can. $	U.K. £
1a	Double caddy	Blue handle; cobalt blue panels, white/gold decoration on top; white with orange/blue and gold on bottom	133	80.00	120.00	60.00

MOTTLED DESIGN

Backstamp:. Black ink stamp "Flaxman Ware Hand made Pottery by Wadeheath England"

No.	Description	Colourways	Size	U.S. $	Can. $	U.K. £
1	Double caddy	Mottled brown/green/yellow	133	60.00	90.00	45.00

TEA CHEST, 1995

Produced for Boots The Chemist, this tea caddy is shaped as a tea chest with a miniature teapot forming the finial of the lid.

T
E
A

C
H
E
S
T

Backstamp: Printed "Wade England" with two lines

No.	Description	Colourways	Size	U.S. $	Can. $	U.K. £
1	Tea chest	Light brown; black lettering and tea leaves "English Breakfast Tea"	127	22.00	30.00	15.00

KITCHENWARE

Not many kitchen/cooking wares were produced by the Wade Potteries, some ovenproof baking dishes and casseroles were produced during the 1970s until c.1995.

SHAPE NAME INDEX

COOKWARE, 1987-1989

A small range of porcelain cookware was produced in a variety of designs and was advertised as "Oven-to-table, microwave, freezer and dishwasher safe."

COUNTRY BLUE DESIGN

Backstamp: **A.** Impressed "Wade England" with printed "Porcelain Cookware Microwave oven and dishwasher safe" the name of the design is included.
B. Impressed "Wade England" with printed "Porcelain Cookware Princess House Copyright 1989 Ltd Microwave oven and dishwasher safe" the name of the design is included

No.	Description	Colourways	Size	U.S. $	Can. $	U.K. £
1	Flan dish	White; blue	230	12.00	15.00	8.00
2	Oval dish		280	12.00	15.00	8.00
3	Pie dish		184	8.00	12.00	6.00
4	Ramekin		50	4.00	6.00	3.00
5	Rectangular roaster		273	15.00	18.00	10.00
6	Shell dish		146	4.00	6.00	3.00

COUNTRY HARVEST DESIGN

Backstamp: Impressed "Wade England" with printed "Porcelain Cookware Princess House Copyright 1989 Ltd. Microwave oven and dishwasher safe" the name of the design is included

No.	Description	Colourways	Size	U.S. $	Can. $	U.K. £
1	Flan dish	White; orange fruits; green leaves/fields	230	12.00	15.00	8.00

HERB COLLECTION DESIGN

Backstamp: **A.** Impressed "Wade England" with printed "Porcelain Cookware Microwave oven and dishwasher safe" the name of the design is included.
B. Impressed "Wade England" with printed "Porcelain Cookware Princess House Copyright 1989 Ltd Microwave oven and dishwasher safe" the name of the design is included

No.	Description	Colourways	Size	U.S. $	Can. $	U.K. £
1	Flan dish	Cream; multi-coloured print	230	12.00	15.00	8.00
2	Oval dish		280	12.00	15.00	8.00
3	Pie dish		184	8.00	12.00	6.00
4	Ramekin		50	4.00	6.00	3.00
5	Rectangular roaster		273	15.00	18.00	10.00
6	Shell dish		146	4.00	6.00	3.00

MULTI-SPLASH DESIGN

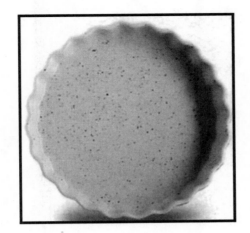

Backstamp: **A.** Impressed "Wade England" with printed "Porcelain Cookware Microwave oven and dishwasher safe" the name of the design is included.
B. Impressed "Wade England" with printed "Porcelain Cookware Princess House Copyright 1989 Ltd Microwave oven and dishwasher safe" the name of the design is included

No.	Description	Colourways	Size	U.S. $	Can. $	U.K. £
1	Flan dish	White; coloured spots	230	12.00	15.00	8.00
2	Oval dish		280	12.00	15.00	8.00
3	Pie dish		184	8.00	12.00.	6.00
4	Ramekin		50	4.00	6.00	3.00
5	Rectangular roaster		273	15.00	18.00	10.00
6	Shell dish		146	4.00	6.00	3.00

WHITE DESIGN

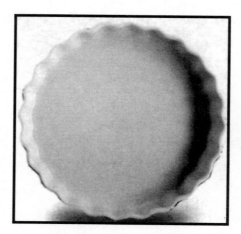

Backstamp: A. Impressed "Wade England" with printed "Porcelain Cookware Microwave oven and dishwasher safe" the name of the design is included.
B. Impressed "Wade England" with printed "Porcelain Cookware Princess House Copyright 1989 Ltd Microwave oven and dishwasher safe" the name of the design is included

No.	Description	Colourways	Size	U.S. $	Can. $	U.K. £
1	Flan dish	White	230	8.00	10.00	5.00
2	Oval dish		280	8.00	10.00	5.00
3	Pie dish		184	6.00	8.00	4.00
4	Ramekin		50	3.00	4.00	2.00
5	Rectangular roaster		273	10.00	12.00	6.00
6	Shell dish		146	3.00	4.00	2.00

COUNTRYWARE, c.1978-1984

These cookware items were produced in the Wade Ireland Pottery, Portadown, Northern Ireland. For matching cruets see page 337, for matching storage jars see page 397.

Backstamp: Impressed circular "Design Wade Country Ware Made in Ireland"

No.	Description	Irish Wade No.	Colourways	Size	U.S. $	Can. $	U.K. £
1	Casserole, 3 ½ pint	KD1	Amber	159	25.00	35.00	18.00
2	Casserole, 2 pint	KD9		146	20.00	30.00	15.00

Country Blue Cookware

CHILDREN'S NURSERY WARES
c.1935-c.1952

Whenever a subject attracted the attention of the general public, the Wade potteries were quick to imitate it on their nursery wares with colourful transfer prints that illustrated well-known characters from a children's book, a television series or a current Walt Disney cartoon film. A limited number of Walt Disney's novelty cartoon characters were re-created on children's nursery dishes by Wadeheath during the mid 1930s-early 1950s. Disney related products usually have the name "Walt Disney" included in the backstamp, but a few have been found that only have a "Wadeheath England" or "Made in England" backstamp. On most items the name Walt Disney appears in the print next to the character depicted.

1949 Advertisement for Quack-Quacks Nursery Wares

LULLABY LAND WALT DISNEY CHARACTERS, c.1940

This child's plate has three Walt Disney characters depicted on it with the name "Walt Disney" printed underneath each print, the plate does not have a Walt Disney backstamp.

Backstamp: Black ink stamp "Wade Heath England" with "A" added (round W 1939-1945)

No.	Description	Colourways	Size	U.S. $	Can. $	U.K. £
1	Plate	Cream; orange rim; multi-coloured prints of Little Hiawatha, Funny Little Bunnies, Fawn	165	90.00	120.00	60.00

MICKEY MOUSE NURSERY WARE SET, 1934

Although Wadeheath advertising shows these items as a boxed set of four pieces, a heavy baby plate, a clipped corner plate and a cup and saucer, a fifth piece, an oatmeal bowl with clipped corners has been found. With each four piece boxed set the purchaser received a free babies mug.

Produced in two background colours, cream or white, each set has different Mickey and Minnie Mouse, Donald Duck, Pluto and other Disney character transfer prints.

Backstamp: A. Ink stamp "Wadeheath Ware made in England manufactured by permission Walt Disney Mickey Mouse LTD"
B. Ink stamp "Wadeheath Ware by Permission Walt Disney Mickey Mouse LTD made in England"

No.	Description	Colourways	Size	U.S. $	Can. $	U.K. £
1a	Baby plate	Cream; multi-coloured print of Mickey and Pluto	153	90.00	120.00	60.00
1b	Baby plate	White; yellow print of Pluto		90.00	120.00	60.00
2a	Cup	White; multi-coloured print of Mickey walking	63	45.00	60.00	30.00
2b	Cup	White; multi-coloured print of Mickey holding out hand	63	45.00	60.00	30.00
2c	Cup	White; multi-coloured print of Minnie with mirror	63	45.00	60.00	30.00
3a	Mug	White; multi-coloured print of Donald with fishing rod	82	60.00	80.00	40.00
3b	Mug	White; multi-coloured print of Mickey holding out hand	82	60.00	80.00	40.00
3c	Mug	White; multi-coloured print of Minnie with mirror	82	60.00	80.00	40.00
4a	Oatmeal bowl, clipped corners	White; multi-coloured print of Mickey walking	63	85.00	110.00	55.00
5a	Plate	White; multi-coloured print of Donald peanut vender	146	90.00	120.00	60.00
5b	Plate	White; multi-coloured print of Donald and Pluto	146	90.00	120.00	60.00
5c	Plate	White; multi-coloured print of Mickey and Horse Collar	146	90.00	120.00	60.00
5d	Plate	White; multi-coloured print of Minnie and Mickey	146	90.00	120.00	60.00
6	Saucer	Cream; multi-coloured print of Mickey and puppy	144	35.00	50.00	25.00

NODDY AND BIG EARS NURSERY WARE, 1955

This set has transfer prints of characters from Enid Blyton's *Noddy and Big Ears* storybook characters which were first published in 1953. In the mid 1950s Noddy and Big Ears became a much loved B.B.C. television cartoon series. The baby plate has a thick raised rim and is heavy so that it stays in place more easily.

Photograph of this
design not available
at press time

Backstamp: Printed "Wade England © 1953 by Noddy Subsidiary Rights Co. Ltd"

No.	Description	Colourways	Size	U.S. $	Can. $	U.K. £
1	Baby plate	White; multi-coloured print of Noddy and his car	177	60.00	80.00	40.00
2	Beaker, no handle	White; multi-coloured print of Big Ears and Noddy	80	45.00	60.00	30.00
3	Beaker, with handle	White; multi-coloured print of Big Ears with balloons	80	45.00	60.00	30.00
4	Cup/saucer	Cup — white; multi-coloured print of golliwog Saucer —white; multi-coloured print of Noddy	63/144	35.00	45.00	20.00
5	Mug	White; multi-coloured print of Big Ears with balloons	82	45.00	60.00	30.00
6	Oatmeal bowl	White; multi-coloured print of Big Ears and Noddy	159	55.00	70.00	35.00
7	Plate	White; multi-coloured print of Big Ears with balloons	146	60.00	80.00	40.00

NODDY AND BIG EARS

PANDA AND PANDY NURSERY WARE, 1939

As a result of the arrival of the baby panda Ming Ming at the London Zoo on Christmas Eve, 1938 Wadeheath produced two sets of nursery ware with a Panda as the central design.

P
A
N
D
A

A
N
D

P
A
N
D
Y

PANDA

The band on this design is wider than that found on the Pandy design.

Photograph of this
design not available
at press time

Backstamp: Green ink stamp "Wade Heath England" (round W 1937-1940)

No.	Description	Colourways	Size	U.S. $	Can. $	U.K. £
1	Baby plate	White; green band; black and white panda sitting; black lettering	171	60.00	80.00	40.00
2	Beaker		88	40.00	50.00	25.00
3	Cup and saucer	White; green band; black and white panda walking; black lettering	63/144	45.00	60.00	30.00
4	Mug		82	40.00	50.00	25.00
5	Plate	White; green band; black and white panda sitting; black lettering	153	60.00	80.00	40.00

PANDY

The panda bear on this design is shown, when seated, with a ball.

Backstamp: Green ink stamp "Wade Heath England" (round W 1937-1940)

No.	Description	Colourways	Size	U.S. $	Can. $	U.K. £
1	Baby plate	White; green band/grass; black and white sitting pandy; black lettering; black ball with green stripes	171	60.00	80.00	40.00
2	Beaker		88	40.00	50.00	25.00
3	Cup and saucer	White; green band/grass; black and white walking pandy; black lettering	63/144	45.00	60.00	30.00
4	Mug		82	40.00	50.00	25.00
5	Plate	White; green band/grass; black and white sitting pandy; black lettering; black ball with green stripes	153	60.00	80.00	40.00

PINOCCHIO NURSERY WARE, 1940

The Pinocchio set was advertised in April 1940. A Children's Toy Tea Set (see page 425) was available at the same time, both sets have transfer prints of characters from the Walt Disney cartoon film "Pinocchio."

Photograph of this design
not available at
press time

Backstamp: **A.** Ink stamp "Wadeheath by permission Walt Disney England"
B. Black ink stamp "Made In England"

No.	Description	Colourways	Size	U.S. $	Can. $	U.K. £
1	Cup/saucer	White; multi-coloured print of Pinocchio	63/144	45.00	60.00	30.00
2	Mug	White; multi-coloured print of Jiminy Cricket	82	90.00	120.00	60.00
3	Oatmeal bowl	White; multi-coloured print of Geppetto	153	85.00	110.00	55.00
4	Plate	White; multi-coloured print of Blue Fairy	153	90.00	120.00	60.00

QUACK ! QUACK ! NURSERY WARE, c.1949 - 1957

The set features a Comic Duck family (for Comic Duck figures see *The Charlton Standard Catalogue of Wade Whimsical Collectables*).

Backstamp: Black printed "Quack - Quacks by Robert Barlow Wade England" with a multi-coloured print of Dack pulling at a worm

No.	Description	Colourways	Size	U.S. $	Can. $	U.K. £
1	Baby plate	White; multi-coloured print of Duck family at pond	180	60.00	80.00	40.00
2	Cup	Cup — White; multi-coloured print of Mrs. Duck and Dack (son) at picnic; Saucer —White; multi-coloured print of ducklings around rim	63/144	35.00	45.00	20.00
3	Milk jug , ½ pint	White; multi-coloured print of Mr. and Mrs. Duck holding hands	88	55.00	65.00	35.00
4	Mug	White; multi-coloured print of Mr. and Mrs. Duck holding hands	82	45.00	60.00	30.00
5	Oatmeal bowl	White; multi-coloured print of Mr. and Mrs. Duck talking	159	55.00	65.00	35.00
6	Plate, large	White; multi-coloured print of Duck family at pond	205	60.00	80.00	40.00
7	Plate, small	White; multi-coloured print of Mr. and Mrs. Duck talking	153	55.00	65.00	35.00

P
I
N
O
C
C
H
I
O

SNOW WHITE CHILD'S NURSERY SET, 1938

S
N
O
W

W
H
I
T
E

Backstamp: Ink stamp "Wadeheath by Permission Walt Disney England"

No.	Description	Colourways	Size	U.S. $	Can. $	U.K. £
1	Cup and saucer	Cream; orange rim; multi-coloured print of Bashful with musical instrument	63/144	35.00	45.00	20.00
2	Oatmeal bowl	White; orange rings; multi-coloured print of Happy	153	85.00	110.00	55.00

CHILDREN'S TOY TEA/DINNER SETS
1934 - 1940s

A large number of Toy Tea Sets were produced by Wade Heath in the 1930s. They were produced with hand painted orange bands around the rims, but on a few items the band may be missing having worn or washed off. The sets have an assortment of multi-coloured transfer prints of Walt Disney Cartoon and other nursery rhyme characters on them. Because these sets were all decorated with transfer prints, the prints could be alternated between cups, plates, jugs and sugar bowls (at the decorators whim). It is possible to find sets with different characters than a previous set, i.e. Dopey on a sugar bowl in one set and Thumper on the sugar bowl in another. This rule applies to all the sets issued. The names of the characters are usually included in print in black or red lettering.

Design Name Index

BAMBI AND SNOW WHITE AND THE SEVEN DWARFS, 1938

This set depicted a different Walt Disney character on each piece. Thumper and Bambi appear on the milk jug, sugar bowl, saucers and tureen. The dwarfs (Bashful, Doc, Grumpy, Happy, Sleepy and Sneezy) are featured on the teacups. In some sets, the seventh dwarf (Dopey) is pictured with Snow White.

Backstamp: A. Black ink stamp "Wadeheath by permission Walt Disney, England"
B. Green ink stamp "Wade Heath England" (Tureen only)

No.	Description	Colourways	Size	U.S. $	Can. $	U.K. £
1	Cup and saucer	White; multi-coloured print	46/95	150.00	200.00	85.00
2	Milk jug		50	75.00	100.00	60.00
3	Plate, large		130	75.00	100.00	60.00
4	Plate, medium	White; orange band; multi-coloured print	120	75.00	100.00	60.00
5	Plate, small		105	75.00	100.00	60.00
6	Sugar bowl		35	75.00	100.00	60.00
7	Teapot		85	100.00	135.00	85.00
8	Tureen		72 x 130	155.00	205.00	105.00

BERRIES

Backstamp: Black ink stamp "England" (c.1938)

No.	Description	Colourways	Size	U.S. $	Can. $	U.K. £
1	Cup and saucer	White; red berries, green leaves on cup; green leaves and orange bands on saucer	48	50.00	60.00	30.00
2	Milk jug	White; red berries; green leaves	50	30.00	40.00	20.00
3	Plate		120	25.00	35.00	18.00
4	Sugar bowl		35	25.00	40.00	20.00
5	Teapot		85	55.00	70.00	35.00

FLORAL

This set has a transfer printed design of small flowers and leaves.

Photograph of this
design not available
at press time

Backstamp: Black ink stamp "England" (c.1938)

No.	Description	Colourways	Size	U.S. $	Can. $	U.K. £
1	Cup and saucer	White; multi-coloured print	46/95	50.00	60.00	30.00
2	Milk jug		50	30.00	40.00	20.00
3	Plate		130	25.00	35.00	18.00
4	Sugar bowl		35	25.00	40.00	20.00
5	Teapot		85	55.00	70.00	35.00

LULLABY LAND, c.1938

This childrens tea set features characters from Walt Disney shorts (short cartoon films). Walt Disney and the names of the characters are printed in black lettering.

Transfer prints:

A. Elmer Elephant

D. Lullaby Land (sleeping boy)

B. Funny Little Bunnies

E. Thumper

C. Little Hiawatha

Backstamp: Ink stamp "Wadeheath by Permission Walt Disney England"

No.	Description	Colourways	Size	U.S. $	Can. $	U.K. £
1	Cup and saucer	Cup —white; multi-coloured print; Saucer — white with orange bands	46/95	70.00	95.00	40.00
2	Milk jug	White; multi-coloured print	50	60.00	70.00	30.00
3	Plate		130	50.00	65.00	25.00
4	Sugar bowl		35	60.00	70.00	30.00
5	Teapot		85	100.00	135.00	50.00

MICKEY MOUSE, 1935

This tea set, for either four or six, was available with a variety of prints. A variety of transfer prints were used on all the pieces in a particular set. Multiple designs were sometimes used on the same piece. For example, Minnie reading a letter and Pluto barking.

Transfer prints:

A. Donald Duck dancing a sailor's jig
C. Donald Duck as peanut vendor
E. Mickey Mouse with envelope
G. Mickey Mouse as Jack
I. Mickey Mouse walking
K. Minnie Mouse reading a letter
M. Pluto barking

B. Donald Duck as Little Boy Blue
D. Mickey Mouse dancing
F. Mickey Mouse sitting
H. Mickey Mouse digging
J. Minnie Mouse as Jill
L. Minnie Mouse with mirror
N. Minnie, Mickey and Donald Duck dancing
  "Ring a Ring of Roses"

Backstamp: A. Black circular ink stamp "Wadeheath Ware by permission Walt Disney Mickey Mouse Ltd Made in England"
B. Ink stamp "Wadeheath by Permission Walt Disney England"

No.	Description	Colourways	Size	U.S. $	Can. $	U.K. £
1	Cup and saucer	White; multi-coloured prints	46/95	80.00	105.00	50.00
2	Milk jug		50	60.00	70.00	30.00
3	Plate		130	50.00	65.00	25.00
4	Sugar bowl		35	60.00	70.00	30.00
5	Teapot		85	100.00	135.00	50.00
6	Boxed set for 4		—	850.00	1,200.00	500.00
7	Boxed set for 6		—	1,200.00	1,500.00	650.00

NURSERY RHYMES, c.1935

A variety of nursery rhyme verses are printed in black lettering on these pieces.

Transfer prints:

A. ABC Tumble Down
C. Little Jumping Joan
E. Simple Simon Met a Pieman

B. Ding Dong Bell, Pussy's in the Well
D. Ring a Roses
F. What are Little Girls Made of

Photograph of this
design not available
at press time

Backstamp: **A.** Ink stamp "Wade Heath England"
B. Ink stamp "England"
C. Unmarked

No.	Description	Colourways	Size	U.S. $	Can. $	U.K. £
1	Cup and saucer	White; multi-coloured print; black lettering	46/95	80.00	105.00	50.00
2	Milk jug		50	60.00	70.00	30.00
3	Plate		130	50.00	65.00	25.00
4	Sugar bowl		35	60.00	70.00	30.00
5	Teapot		85	100.00	135.00	50.00

PINOCCHIO, 1940

This set was advertised in April 1940. A Children's Nursery Ware Set was available at the same time, both sets have transfer prints of characters from the Walt Disney cartoon film *Pinocchio*.

Transfer Prints:

A. Blue Fairy
D. Geppetto
G. Strombolis Parrot

B. Donkey
E. Jiminy Cricket

C. Figaro the Cat
F. Pinocchio

Photograph of this
design not available
at press time

Backstamp: Ink stamp "Wadeheath by Permission Walt Disney England"

No.	Description	Colourways	Size	U.S. $	Can. $	U.K. £
1	Cup and saucer	White; multi-coloured print	46/95	80.00	105.00	50.00
2	Milk jug		50	60.00	70.00	30.00
3	Plate		130	50.00	65.00	25.00
4	Sugar bowl	White; orange band; multi-coloured print	35	60.00	70.00	30.00
5	Teapot	White; multi-coloured print	85	100.00	135.00	50.00

PRUDENCE THE CAT, c.1935

Backstamp: Black ink stamp "England"

No.	Description	Colourways	Size	U.S. $	Can. $	U.K. £
1	Cup and saucer	White; red/white/grey print	46/95	50.00	60.00	30.00
2	Milk jug		50	30.00	40.00	20.00
3	Plate		130	25.00	35.00	18.00
4	Sugar bowl		35	25.00	40.00	20.00
5	Teapot		85	55.00	70.00	35.00

UNKNOWN SET

The print on the following sugar bowl is of a baby seal wearing a bobbled hat and blowing a trumpet, the name "Baby Seal" and Walt Disney are under the print. This character is believed to have been the one on which the large Walt Disney model "Sammy Seal" was based. Baby Seal is featured in a Disney short.

Backstamp: Ink stamp "Wadeheath By Permission Walt Disney England"

No.	Description	Colourways	Size	U.S. $	Can. $	U.K. £
1	Sugar bowl	White; brown/orange/yellow print	35	60.00	70.00	30.00

MISCELLANEOUS ITEMS

SHAPE NAME INDEX

CLASSIC KINGS/KINGS TOAST RACK, 1992-1993

For an illustration
of this design
see page 328

For other items in this set please see pages 307, 331, 336, 337, 343, 349 and 397.

Backstamp: Printed "Wade England" with two lines

No.	Description	Colourways	Size	U.S. $	Can. $	U.K.£
1a	Toast rack	Cream	76	8.00	10.00	5.00
1b	Toast rack	Dark green; gold edging	76	8.00	10.00	5.00
1c	Toast rack	White	76	8.00	10.00	5.00
1d	Toast rack	White; gold edging	76	8.00	10.00	5.00

CORKSCREW SEALION, 1960

First issued in January 1960, this corkscrew is a sealion balancing a coloured striped ball on his nose. The ball is the handle of the corkscrew which slides down inside the hollow nose. Unmarked, but originally issuedwith a black and gold "Genuine Wade Porcelain" paper label on base.

Backstamp: Paper label "Genuine Wade Porcelain"

No.	Description	Colourways	Size	U.S. $	Can. $	U.K.£
1a	Corkscrew	Grey brown sealion; white, yellow and blue ball	145 x 80	120.00	160.00	80.00
1b	Corkscrew	Grey brown sealion; white, green, red and blue ball	145 x 80	120.00	160.00	80.00
1c	Corkscrew	Grey brown sealion; white, pink, blue and green ball	145 x 80	120.00	160.00	80.00

CRUMB BRUSH GUARDSMAN, c.1952

Wade produced a Guardsman crumb brush formed as the head and shoulders of a "moustached" Grenadier Guardsman. Found with red, white and blue bristles and also with brown bristles. It is possible the Guardsman may have been intended as a London souvenir. The Guardsman, which has thirteen holes in the base for the brush bristles, is most often found without the bristles which have loosened and fallen out. There is a slanted hole in the back of the head for hanging the brush on a nail.

Backstamp: Impressed "Registered No. 869473 Made in England" in recess on back of figure

No.	Description	Colourways	Size	U.S. $	Can. $	U.K.£
1a	Crumb brush	Beige	80 x 65	60.00	80.00	40.00
1b	Crumb brush	Honey brown	80 x 65	60.00	80.00	40.00
1c	Crumb brush	Light blue	80 x 65	60.00	80.00	40.00
1d	Crumb brush	Light green	80 x 65	60.00	80.00	40.00
1e	Crumb brush	Pink	80 x 65	60.00	80.00	40.00

FALSTAFF SUGAR BOWL, c.1972

Falstaff Ware has been found in royal blue and white with red roses, the royal blue is the most commonly seen colour. Wade produced the porcelain part of the Falstaff wares, the silver plated lids with "Rose Bud" finials and "Lion Mask" handles were attached by the Falstaff Silver Plating Co which was based in Birmingham. As well as the sugar bowl, a claret jug (see page 291-292), honey pot (see page 350) and rose bowl (see *The Charlton Standard Catalogue of Wade Volume Two: Decorative Ware*) were also produced.

VERSION ONE — WITH HANDLES

For an illustration
of this design
see page 291

Backstamp: Embossed "Wade Falstaff England" plus label "Falstaff Silver Plated Collection"

No.	Description	Colourways	Size	U.S. $	Can. $	U.K.£
1	Sugar bowl	Royal blue; silver plated lid, lion mask handles/lid	130	55.00	65.00	30.00

VERSION TWO — WITHOUT HANDLES

For an illustration
of this design
see page 292

Backstamp: Embossed "Wade Falstaff England" plus label "Falstaff Silver Plated Collection"

No.	Description	Colourways	Size	U.S. $	Can. $	U.K.£
1	Sugar bowl	White; red roses print; silver plated lid	130	55.00	65.00	30.00

FALSTAFF

RAMEKINS, 1997

Backstamp: Unknown

No.	Description	Colourways	Size	U.S. $	Can. $	U.K.£
1a	Badger family	White; multi-coloured print	101	6.00	8.00	4.00
1b	Christmas wreath		101	5.00	7.00	3.00
1c	Deer family		101	6.00	8.00	4.00
1d	Fruit (currants)		101	5.00	7.00	3.00
1e	Grey squirrel family		101	6.00	8.00	4.00
1f	Otter family		101	6.00	8.00	4.00
1g	Stag family (1 fawn)		101	6.00	8.00	4.00
1h	Stag family (2 fawns)		101	6.00	8.00	4.00

STEAK KNIVES

These unusual steak knives have pretty transfer printed porcelain handles. There are no Wade marks on the knives but the box is marked: "Regent Sheffield, The Greatest Name in Cutlery. Finest English Porcelain Handles Made in England By Wade."

Backstamp: None

No.	Description	Colourways	Size	U.S. $	Can. $	U.K.£
1	Steak knives	White handle; blue leaves; small orange/pink/yellow flowers	210	125.00	165.00	85.00

Note: The price is for a set of six boxed knives.

SUGAR CASTER, c.1934-1937

This unusual sugar caster is cone shaped.

Backstamp: Black ink stamp "Wadeheath Ware England" (1934-1937)

No.	Description	Colourways	Size	U.S. $	Can. $	U.K.£
1	Sugar caster	Streaked blue grey/cream/orange	125	30.00	40.00	20.00

TOAST RACK

This toast rack was produced as a Christmas line. See page 355 for a matching preserve pot.

Backstamp: Printed red circular "Royal Victoria Pottery Staffordshire Wade England"

No.	Description	Colourways	Size	U.S. $	Can. $	U.K.£
1	Toast rack	White; multi-coloured print of partridge in a pear tree	76	10.00	15.00	8.00

Design Name Index